CELEBRATING LIFE
AFTER OVERCOMING AN
EATING DISORDER

CAROLINE B. COOK

Fedd Books
P.O. Box 341973
Austin, TX 78734
www.thefeddagency.com

Published in association with The Fedd Agency, Inc., a literary agency.

Design by Deryn Pieterse

ISBN: 978-1-957616-06-3
eISBN: 978-1-957616-07-0
Library of Congress Number: 2022906631

Printed in the United States of America
First Edition 22 23 24 25 /6 5 4 3 2

To the Cook Girls...Annie, Rawlie and Wesley

TABLE OF CONTENTS

FOREWORD BY SARAH ROSE SUMMERS, MISS USA 2018

Imagine becoming the first Miss USA from your home state; an unattainable dream that suddenly became reality. Overnight, you're uprooted and moved from Nebraska to a high-rise in New York City. It's surreal, a bit of a fairytale even. Just four months later, you get to live another dream, to walk in New York Fashion Week, basically the Super Bowl of fashion! You strut your stuff down the runway with friends in the audience and family watching the live stream back home. You feel on top of the world. After the show you open social media and suddenly that joy and confidence you felt walking down the runway is ripped out from under you.

> *Oink oink oink* *pig emoji* *pig emoji* *pig emoji*"
> *Miss USA is fat.*
> *She's more than a curvy girl, she's fat.*
> *You're disgusting - need diet.*

Countless body shaming comments and direct messages flooded my social media after walking in NYFW as Miss USA. This was my reality, and I was ashamed. I wanted to enjoy the high after walking off stage but, much like Caroline becoming homecoming queen, my thoughts, too, were consumed by my weight. I wanted the designer and the Miss Universe Organization to be proud but how could they be with this as the response on social media?

When I was younger, back in 2011, I competed in my first pageant with a swimsuit portion and for the first time in my life I began a 'diet.' Leading up to the pageant, I had a sponsor who provided workout plans and a very strict diet plan that I can still recite today, even 10 years later. No one told me I didn't have to follow it, or if they did, I didn't truly hear it. Nearing the pageant, I surpassed discipline to the point of obsession. If I ate fifteen instead of my allotted twelve almonds, I would fall asleep thinking about those three almonds. As Caroline mentions, it's easy to cover up an eating disorder with the false sense of 'discipline.' Does this sound familiar for you? To my surprise I won Miss Nebraska Teen USA and the swimsuit award, but it is another example of the pressures and mentality I experienced regarding my body even before my time as Miss USA.

The unfortunate truth is that my experience isn't an isolated incident. Both celebrities and Midwest teenagers alike face body shaming and cyberbullying on a regular basis. I believe these types of comments are a major factor in contributing to our distorted ideals of beauty. The week following NYFW, I chose to respond to the haters with a public announcement, not only for myself but for all the girls and women reading the comments and wondering "if she's fat, then what am I?"

I truly believe that if I had let myself sit in those comments, if I had been hungry for the approval of people that didn't matter, it could have led me back to the time of disordered eating habits. I could have missed the impact and plans God had in store for my year as Miss USA.

It is no secret that we live in a broken and hurting world. Eating disorders are the number one fatal mental illness in our country, with nearly one person dying every hour. That means, we are some of the lucky ones. Maybe you're struggling with your own eating disorder, your idea of what you should look like, or the worlds, but trust in God, our ultimate healer, and trust in yourself.

We cannot continue to tiptoe around these issues, ones that girls everywhere are facing. We need to love each other and ourselves better. It's okay to share your stories and ask for help. I have no doubt that though Caroline's stories and the glimpses of His truth in the pages to follow, you will find understanding and the truth that you are not alone. It is my sincerest hope that Hungry will make you feel understood, worthy, and full of hope.

- Sarah

LETTER TO
THE READER

"If someone had told me what this road would look like, I don't think I would have gone this way."

These are the words I said to myself when I started recovering from my eating disorder over twenty-five years ago. I knew I had to tell my story. I wanted to make sure others knew what this lifestyle was really like, so that maybe they would choose another path. Just like a bright yellow danger sign can warn travelers to turn around, I'm trying to tell you that this way is not safe. An eating disorder leads to hurt and heartache. It can even take your life.

Though I was ready to shout my story from the rooftops twenty-five years ago, life took an unexpected detour. I fell head over heels in love. Our courtship was fast and furious, and we were married a little over a year later. And since we obviously don't waste time, we welcomed a baby girl into the world a year after that. And then another girl, and another girl, and then a little boy rounded out our family of six. In other words, my life got really busy! And the dream of writing a book about my recovery was put on hold. But now those four babies are much older, and it's a good time to take this on. The desire to tell my story has only grown with time. In fact, I think I now have more to say than ever.

As soon as we are born, we are hungry. One of my favorite memories is a moment after I had my first child. "Somebody's hungry," the nurse whispered as she wheeled the small portable crib into my darkened hospital room. It felt like the most important person in the world was coming toward me, needing me, wanting the sustenance that only a nursing mother could provide. She wanted *me*. And it was her hunger that brought her there.

Have you ever thought about why we were designed to be hungry? God could have made us any way He wanted, but He chose for us to be a needy bunch. And I have a strong suspicion as to why an appetite for daily food was part of His plan.

Hunger is what brings my family of six to the kitchen together, where best conversations take place. Where our life happens. Hunger is what prompts my husband to call or text at about four in the afternoon most days, just wanting me to whet his appetite with our dinner plans or brainstorm about the possible menu. Hunger is what brings us to the table with friends and family. It is what prompts us to plan a meal to share and get to know each other, to invest in one another. And our hunger reflects our need. God could have designed our bodies any way He wanted to. He made the rules. And He made us to be hungry *every day*. He could have easily decided that our hunger was to be satisfied once a week, once a month, or maybe once a year. But no, in His wisdom He made us to need food on a daily basis. It reminds us of our daily need of Him as well.

Jesus said, "I am the bread of life; whoever comes to me shall not hunger, and whoever believes in me shall never thirst" (John 6:35). This analogy was not a mistake. This is Jesus connecting the dots for us. We need food, and we need Him. We know we need to feed our bodies daily, but He is reminding us that our souls and hearts need to be fed by Him every day as well.

I have lived in recovery now for a long time. Writing this book has been an up-close and personal reminder of where I once was and where I am now. I once was lost and now I am found. Praise God! In the next fourteen chapters, I hope you see how God pursued me again and again. He doesn't hold grudges. Even after I ran away from Him time and time again, He loved me enough to show me how my ways were not working and how His ways did work. They always do.

This story is also about important moments in our lives that shape us into who we are. Our families, words spoken to us, experiences we have, and mistakes we make. Because we all make mistakes. But here you see that He can use those mistakes for good. I hope you see that change is possible, even when it feels impossible. I certainly thought it was out of the question for me to get better. And maybe you do too. But God doesn't. It starts with a step of faith. Just one. One decision, and then another one, and then hopefully one after that. The road is long, but each step you take matters. Just like daily bread, there are daily decisions. And over time these decisions take you down a path and determine your life. I love the wise mantra my children recited every morning at their elementary school flag raising:

> Watch your thoughts, they become your words.
> Watch your words, they become your actions.
> Watch your actions, they become your habits.
> Watch your habits, they become your character.
> Watch your character, for it becomes your destiny.[1]

Whoever you are reading this book, I am honored to have you along for the telling of my story. I hope you can see a little of yourself in it.

Being hungry is part of the master plan. His loving and good plan. It brings us to the table, where a lot of good stuff happens. So come. Sit. Hear how He worked a miracle in me. Read how I never, ever thought I would live free of an eating disorder. But with God all things are possible, and He is in the business of miracles. He's crazy about me. And I can promise you He is crazy about you too.

ALONE IN MADRID

It is one thing to feel lonely when you are by yourself, but it is another to long for connection when you are surrounded by crowds of people. I was experiencing the latter. Walking along the busy streets of Madrid, I had never felt so utterly alone.

Cars and strangers raced by me on their way to work, but I walked slowly and nervously contemplating what I had just done. I had made a monumental decision. One that would change everything about my life. A decision that led to health, and life, and freedom. So why did I feel so terrified?

Every few minutes I would stop and pull a tattered and torn piece of paper from my front pocket. I would hold on to this lifeline and read it over and over again. Remind myself of what I was going to do. Or at least of what I wanted to want to do. I needed to remember all the reasons why I wasn't going to live like this anymore.

I had made this life-changing decision just a few days prior. I hadn't told a soul yet. I was scared to! Once I told them they would hold me accountable, and I wasn't sure I could make any promises yet. At least not to anyone else. This was going to be a leap of faith. A leap I wasn't entirely sure I was ready to make.

I knew that what I was doing wasn't good. I knew that life was supposed to be lived a different way, but this was scary. I had gotten used to my unhealthy ways. This was just who I was now. Who was I without an eating disorder? Would I be just like everyone else? And why did it bother me to be like everyone else? It was all so confusing. But this little piece of paper did make sense to me. It reminded me of the *why*. Why I had decided to change. And every time I pulled it out and read it I remembered. It told my fearful heart and mind the truth. There weren't many benefits of living with an eating disorder. In fact, there was only one.

PRO	CON
• Skinny	• not healthy
	• might not be able to have kids
	• hard to be married
	• God doesn't want this for me
	• you live ensnared by it
	• steals your joy
	• hard to enjoy life
	• bad for relationships
	• might kill you over time
	• I know better

The con side was long and it could have been much longer. It stared at me like a blinking danger sign, begging me to see the obvious reasons to stop this craziness. This dangerous obsession. I knew this list was truthful and good—I wrote it for crying out loud—but I had to look at it again and again. Daring myself to believe it. *Can I do this? Do I want to do this?* Yes, I did want to lay down this idol. This life of control and fear and rules. I knew God wanted more for me, so why couldn't I just do it? Why was this so hard?

An eating disorder is a lot like digging a hole. The longer you live in that eating disorder, the deeper the hole gets. And the deeper the hole is, the harder it is to get out. I had spent several years digging this hole, so it was going to take some time if I was going to get out of it. This dark hole was lonely, but it did feel safe. A life of control and rules and fear kept me insulated and alone in a comfortable world of isolation. Away from real life and joy and freedom.

But now I was at a crossroads. *I want to do this. I don't want to do this. I believe you God. Help me believe you.*

Thank goodness I am not the only one who has uttered this phrase. It gives me great peace that a scene in the Bible depicts this exact sentiment. In the ninth chapter of Mark, there is a desperate father who approached Jesus with his sick child. "If you can do anything," he said to Jesus, "have compassion on us and help us." Jesus responded, "'If you can!' All things are possible for one who believes." Then the honest father uttered, "I believe; help my unbelief!" (vv. 22–24). I love this sentence. It is brutally honest. I know what this father feels like. I think most of us do. And that was how I felt, and I knew I wasn't alone.

In these next chapters you will see what led up to this moment on the street in Madrid when I wrestled with this life-changing decision. You may be there too. Or maybe you know someone who is wrestling with a big decision like this. Keep reading and see how I got there. And what road I ended up taking. And where I am now. Come see why I think it is hunger that brings out the best in all of us.

SHE'S GOT IT

I've never met a stage or a microphone I didn't like.

Now before you think I am an obnoxious narcissist, just know that I came out of the womb ravenous for an audience. It's a burden in some ways, but I prefer to think of it as a gift. Public speaking is the number one fear for most people, but not for this girl! Give me a crowd and I'll give you a show. This gift can also come with some unique challenges. A young undiscovered actress must come to grips with the fact that life isn't always a captive audience.

Here are just a few real-life memories that will prove my perpetual desire for a stage:

I had a nightgown that I only wore on the nights Miss America was airing. I pretended it was my evening gown. It was long and silky and made me feel like I was a contestant. Sigh.

I dressed up as a movie star for Career Day in Kindergarten. They paraded our class of costume-clad five-year-olds through the entire elementary school on this important day. Firemen, doctors, athletes.

But I am almost certain I was the only movie star. I still remember some of the older kids laughing as I walked by in my dark sunglasses and bright red lipstick. I remember thinking, "This is no laughing matter. I *will* be famous."

I would memorize the entire score of a musical before I saw it, just in case a member of the cast suddenly fell ill. Then, when they asked the audience if anyone could stand in for the sick cast member, I would be ready! Realistic, right? I knew at a young age that the show must go on! And I knew I could save the day!

In preschool, I invited a boy named Donny over to play after school. We weren't actually friends, but I wanted to pretend I was Marie, so I needed a Donny. Everyone knew about the pop star sensations Donny and Marie Osmond during the late 1970s. Google them if you have no idea what I'm talking about. I was just sure that if I got him in a room with my pretend plastic microphone, he would follow in his namesake's footsteps and belt into song! Let's just say that didn't happen. I was terribly disappointed he was not a singer. I am sure he was just as disappointed in our playdate.

I remember crying myself to sleep at night because I wanted to be on Broadway so badly. I refused to believe that my calm, brunette mother was my biological mother. I truly begged my parents to tell me that I was not their natural-born child! I was just sure some theatrical blonde actress had given me up for adoption. My parents just seemed way too normal for me to be related to them. It was disappointing to accept that these regular people really were my parents.

So you will understand the elation I felt when the iconic Broadway star Tommy Tune said these three powerful words to me at a very young age:

"She's got it!"

Let me explain . . .

My grandmother Teenie, my mom, and I loved Broadway musicals. The national tours of these shows would come to Dallas every summer. Several times the three of us would drive three hours north from our home in Austin to attend. We would stay with our dear friends the Snyders in Highland Park, a fancy part of Dallas that the diva in me very much enjoyed. That specific summer we went to see the Tony Award–winning show *My One and Only*. The star of the show was Tommy Tune, whom Teenie had befriended a few years earlier at a Junior League event. This amazing, six-foot-six, larger-than-life celebrity invited us to come back and visit with him after the show. Teenie was the type of person that knew everyone—she also had a larger-than-life personality—so I wasn't ultra-surprised that we had managed to wiggle our way backstage. "This could be my big break," I remember thinking as we were ushered into his private dressing room.

"Teenie!" Tommy hollered in his loud Texas drawl as he jumped up to greet us. My mom and I carefully followed behind Teenie into his cozy dressing room, knowing this was off-limits to about everyone in the world but us. I was pinching myself!

"Oh Tommy, you were just fabulous! The whole show was just unreal!" Teenie gushed as they embraced. His tall, lanky frame bent down low to hug my tiny grandmother.

Meeting a Broadway star in his own dressing room was almost more than I could handle. I wanted his life and fame so badly I could almost taste it! Teenie introduced me to Tommy and told him of my love of the stage. He asked me to sing a note or two for him. No problem! I belted out those notes with pride, and excellence, I might add. I had to make sure I was taking advantage of this incredible opportunity. I knew how to shine in front of an audience, and this was showtime!

"Wow, Caroline! You were certainly meant for the stage!" Tommy said to me. "You need to get her into tap lessons," he said, looking over to my mother. Mom and Teenie both nodded, agreeing with whatever directives this legend passed our way. (I'd like to think that my not ever mastering tap is the sole reason I did not have an illustrious career on Broadway. It turned out I was a terrible tapper. Oh well.)

He continued to look me over with a smile and talk to us about my plans moving forward as a budding star. It was then that I received those three words.

"She's got it!" Tommy said with a wink and a nod.

I was finally validated by someone who knew what they were talking about! It was like unwrapping a shiny golden ticket in a Willie Wonka chocolate bar. I felt like Charlie Bucket waving around the ticket and yelling "I got it!" Finally, someone understood what I knew all along.

My first big break came in fourth grade. My sweet teacher Mrs. Boyd had decided to take on the herculean task of directing us in the Broadway sensation *Cats*. I was cast as Grizabella, the older grand dame in the herd of singing felines. I had the privilege of singing "Memory," the iconic and fabulous belt-it-out song. I like to think of it as my first breakthrough performance. Being the star of the show gave me major clout among us ten-year-olds. My mom had lovingly made my white fur costume with hand-sewn rhinestones! Believe it or not, my mother actually went to college with the original Grizabella on Broadway. Because of this personal connection I wrote her a letter and invited her to our school's performance. She was unable to attend, but on the last day of fourth grade I received a letter from her saying that she hated to miss the show and wished she could have been there. I remember standing on the table reading this fabulous letter to my entire class. No, she didn't come, but she sure wanted to. That was good enough for me! Another check in the box for *I am* going to be a star. Look out world, here I come!

Another memorable role for me was playing Snoopy in *You're a Good Man, Charlie Brown*. Black pants, a white turtleneck, two long blond ponytails on either side of my head, a red dog collar, black converse high-tops, and a black nose were the elements of my simple costume. Snoopy had some fantastic solos. "Suppertime" was my favorite. I know, ironic. This solo required a supersized amount of energy, which was not a problem for this fourteen-year-old teenager/beagle. In one of the performances, I remember thinking, "I *am* a dog." I had reached nirvana as an actress and I *was* my character. We had a video of that performance, and I could point out to those watching the exact moment when I switched from girl to dog. It was a sight to see! I was a gifted Snoopy.

Once I began high school, the roles just got better and better. Our high school theatre program was led by the late Larry Preas and was superb.

Mr. Preas was a beloved and legendary part of our school. His presence was powerful, and he had mastered his craft as a theater teacher. My sophomore year he invited me to his office for a one-on-one chat. His cozy yet eccentric office smelled of cigarettes and coffee. He was sitting in his old leather chair with a pensive look on his face. This was a rare and coveted meeting, reserved for those he felt had a future in the biz. He was hoping he could talk some sense into me. Rumor had it I was about to try out for cheerleader, something Mr. Preas did not advise.

"Caroline, singing could be your bread and butter one day," I vividly remember him telling me. "I really don't want you to risk damaging your voice." He went on to say, "You do a lot of things really well, but you need to pick one thing to be great at."

Pick one? Did he know who he was dealing with? I was in no way going to limit myself to one thing. I very much appreciated his concern and interest in my future, but I had zero interest in choosing one passion. I had dreamed of being a cheerleader my whole life, and I wasn't about to give that up! Surely I could do it all.

Well, I did go on to be a cheerleader during my junior and senior years. I loved it. It was time consuming, and I was less devoted to the theatre during those two years, but it was something I had always dreamed of.

Trying out in front of the entire school was required to make the team. Several thousand people packed into our high school gym on the morning of cheer tryouts. The audience was loud, rowdy, and at times unkind. Just trying out took an insane amount of bravery. I saw it as the hardest stage of them all, but I was hungry for the challenge!

"And now announcing the candidates for 1990 Austin High cheer-leader!" The cheer coach shouted into the mic in front of the massive crowd. I took this as my cue. My last name started with a *B*, so I was first in line to try out. I couldn't get out there fast enough it seemed!

Y'all . . . I ran into the middle of the gym and bounded across the hardwood floor with a gymnastic tumbling routine. As I flip flopped into the middle of the gym, dying to begin my anticipated tryout, our cheer coach said on the mic in front of a zillion people, "Not yet, Caroline! I haven't even introduced you!"

I stopped dead in my tracks. Was this a nightmare? I looked at all those thousands of teenagers dying laughing and said the only thing I could think of.

"Just kidding!"

I ran off the gym floor, dumbfounded at what I had just done, while the audience roared with laughter at my mistake. Then the cheer coach said, "You have seen her once and you will see her again. Come on back out, Caroline Bridges!"

I couldn't believe it, I felt so ridiculous. A friend later told me,

"You proved you are a dumb blonde; you will totally make the team!" And he was right—I did.

So life was good for Caroline Bridges growing up in Austin, Texas. I had a wonderful family, loving parents, a real and powerful relationship with God, a best friend who is still a huge part of my life today as well as other amazing, loyal friends. I had two awesome younger brothers, very involved grandparents. You could say I had it all. But as a senior in high school it was now my turn to enter the world as an adult, to leave the nest and really make my way. The vastness of the opportunities seemed to swallow me up. This was the moment I had been waiting for. Or was it? Where would I go to college? What path would I choose? This was all up to me, and I knew I had one shot to get it right.

Looking ahead, I had few limitations. I had good grades and an impressive resume filled with extracurricular activities. I was looking at competitive colleges all over the country. A good thing, and yet it felt like too many options. How was I to know which path to take? Just like holding your empty plate in front of an enormously scrumptious, all-you-can-eat dinner buffet, I didn't know what to choose. It was overwhelming!

I began to consider the possibilities, but instead of this being fun and exciting, anxiety crept up into my core. What if I picked the wrong college? What if I didn't get in to the right one? Would I be as successful in college as I had been in high school? Would people like me? Would I end up in the "right" sorority? Weren't all these things going to decide my future? My entire life seemed to be relying on this moment in time. I did not have the luxury of failing, or so I thought. I had set the bar so high for myself.

It was time to get serious. It all mattered now. Who I wanted to *be* was at stake, and I knew I wanted to be the best. It was showtime!

And we all know that when the lights dim and the curtains open, the audience is ready and waiting. Would I pursue music and be the next Amy Grant? Or would I go the *Today* show anchor route and be the next Katie Couric? Remember, I only thought big! No mediocrity for this girl!

I loved a challenge, and this was the biggest one yet. And just like a movie star prepares for opening night, I was preparing myself to go before the audience. I wanted to look my best. I desperately wanted to stand out from the rest of the crowd. So how would I accomplish this?

I remembered a time when I had felt extra special a few years before. I had suddenly shed my "baby fat" and was noticed by friends and family alike. It was powerful. I liked the way it made me feel. Powerful felt a whole lot better than feeling unsure of the future.

I started to crave feeling superior to others. I'm not sure I was fully aware of what I was doing, but slowly I began to starve myself. And this burgeoning habit of starvation gave me a feeling of superiority. I was drowning in uncertainty but refusing to eat somehow made me feel more in control. And day by day, skipped meal by skipped meal, this dangerous habit began to eat me alive.

FROZEN TRASH

When I told my childhood best friend Cynda that I was writing this book, she quickly asked,

> "Are you telling them about that weird obsessive thing you did when you literally repeated everything you said?"

No, I wasn't planning on sharing that peculiar memory. But I guess I should. So yes, I will admit that I went through a few very quirky stages as a child. One of them, which she so lovingly reminded me of, took place in about first or second grade. I would say a sentence out loud and then immediately repeat that sentence to myself. Just my lips would move. Yes, you read that correctly. Very odd.

For example, I would ask Cynda, "Hi there, how are you?" and then immediately mouth the words, "Hi there, how are you?" with no sound. Everything had to be said twice. Ugh. I am so thankful

Cynda remained my friend during this unique stage of mine. And I'm sure she would tell you more unusual things I did as well. That's what childhood best friends are for: they remind you of all the weird and wonderful things you did together.

Like the time I was obsessed with my bed being made. Again I was young, elementary school age. If I didn't make my bed before I left for school, which was quite often, I would count on my sweet mother to make it for me. And when I entered my bedroom after school, I would close my eyes and feel the bed to see if it was made. If it wasn't made, I would try and make the bed with my eyes closed. This was all in an attempt to not look at an unmade bed. It was just too upsetting to my sweet little self. I obviously have always had some issues. Don't we all?

The apple didn't fall far from the tree regarding obsessive compulsive idiosyncrasies like these. My precious grandmother Teenie had the unique habit of freezing her trash before she put it out by the street to be collected. Every. Single. Time. I think her hope was that this kept the trash odor from being horrific. You know, so animals wouldn't dig through it. Not a terrible idea if you ask me.

Teenie also had a routine of walking past every appliance in her kitchen before heading out the door to make sure each was in the *off* position. "Off, off, off," she would say in her sing-songy voice. Just double-checking to make sure no house fires would pop up? Yep, that's my Teenie! She just liked to check those boxes.

My dad, Teenie's oldest son, once told me that he struggled with mowing their grass as a young boy. He said that since he couldn't get every blade to be perfect (which is impossible), he just decided it was a lost cause—he flat out couldn't mow it.

So there you have it. I come from people who prefer things nice and neat. Orderly. Would some use the word *perfectionist*? Or *type A*? Maybe. But I also like to think of our kind as creative, strong-willed, and passionate. Perhaps we go a bit too far at times. Perhaps we take ourselves a little too seriously. But, there is a long list of high achievers on this earth who have a little bit of nuttiness in them.

Justin Timberlake, Katy Perry, and soccer sensation David Beckham have all admitted to having obsessive compulsive tendencies. Beckham admits to the need to have everything "just so." When he enters a hotel room, he has to put all leaflets and books in a drawer. I feel you, David. Katy and Justin have talked about the need to have all things perfectly lined up. Nothing crazy, but this compulsion can certainly make life more difficult.[2]

Obsessive Compulsive Tendencies are not a new thing. Charles Dickens, the brilliant author who gave us Scrooge in *A Christmas Carol*, had some interesting habits. Every time he passed a mirror, he had to comb his hair at least one hundred times. He rearranged furniture in his house over and over again and made sure every bed he ever slept in was facing north. It is said that he always carried around a compass because he was so very concerned with magnetic fields.[3] Michelangelo, one of the most famous artists of all times, never bathed. He slept with his boots on even though he admitted they hurt his feet.[4] The list goes on and on. Some of the most interesting and creative people in the world have mental health disorders. And if they can learn to live with this issue, are these people actually carrying around a gift?

I think they are. The question is, how do you use this gift? Do you use it to add to your life or to drive you and others around you crazy? Can you see your funny, weird habits and laugh? Or do others laugh at you because you take yourself so seriously? Questions to ask yourself. Questions I continue to ask myself!

But back to my obsessive tendencies. I knew what it was like to live with an odd habit. I knew how to hyper focus. When I started down the road of an eating disorder it became another ritual, another unusual habit I adopted. Anorexia requires an enormous amount of focus, determination, and passion. You are committing to something that physically hurts. Extreme hunger is really hard. You have to desperately want something if it causes you physical pain. Your goal has to be more important to you than how you feel.

I could taste the determination in me. A constant state of hunger was my new normal.

So it was my senior year of high school. I was the oldest child in the house and the only girl. And I was taking myself very seriously. SAT tutors and AP classes, college visits all over the country, countless meetings with our school college counselor. And then there were the responsibilities at school: endless games to cheer for, choir performances, theatre performances. I was a busy girl! I was getting ready to make the important decision of picking my path and leaving the nest. Forging my own way. Deciding WHO I was and then showing the world exactly what I was made of.

I don't think I knew I was anxious, but looking back that is what it was. There was a heavy weight named anxiety sitting on my chest. The bigness of the unknown left me with a feeling of fear and dread. I didn't have the language then to describe my inner turmoil. I just knew I wanted the feeling of familiarity of back.

Now let me be clear, it is understandable to be apprehensive about the future. Looking into the vast unknown is overwhelming. I don't know many who wouldn't be anxious about that. This is a part of the human experience. We are not given a floodlight to see our whole life ahead, just a lamp. The seventeen-year-old me was dying to be the best. Average was not an option. I didn't just want to do it well—I wanted to hit it out of the park! I liked the feeling of competition.

I liked the challenge of a race to the top. I had been preparing for this moment for years, and I wanted to be the best. But what if I wasn't?

And the pressure. Where did this come from? My parents never told me I had to be the best. My mom was far from being a Tiger Mom who pushed and pushed me to rise to the top. I think it can be confusing for parents when their child feels an intense amount of pressure and they aren't sure of its origin. I know my parents were baffled by it. They saw me constantly adding new "good" things to my schedule. Cheerleading, singing, acting, Young Life. All beneficial things, but when does it become too much of a good thing?

So where does that pressure come from? For me it came from within. No one ever told me I had to be the best; I just wanted to be the best. I was surrounded by successful people. Beautiful people. Not a bad thing, but I knew I wanted to be in this club of high achievers. I wanted to not only climb the ladder but I wanted to sit at the top. I saw two roads ahead of me: one that led to success and one that led to average. And this girl was anything but average.

There is a way to guard yourself from hurt. From not feeling much of anything. No one had ever told me this, but I instinctively knew that by making myself as "perfect" as possible I would be less subject to pain and failure. I began to build invisible walls around myself and my future path. Walls that would shield me from the outside. Walls that were protective and kept me from disappointment. I began to feel insulated from the competitive outside world by creating this new secret lifestyle. The walls became higher and higher with each meal I would skip, pound I would lose, or restriction I would make.

Success was now my only option. I was starving to make my mark on this world, but deep down I now know I was terrified of failing. I didn't know this was a true fear of mine, and I certainly never would have verbalized this to friends or family. What would they say? Get a grip! And don't take yourself so seriously! I could just hear that from those around me. But I did take it seriously, and I felt so radically responsible for my next steps in life. Even though I knew God was in control, I think I felt like my life was out of His realm.

Oh, how I wish I could go back and tell the young Caroline that no one expected perfection. Perfection is not only impossible but an illusion. Life is a series of trial and errors. All we can do is take one day at a time. There is no such thing as a perfect path. I'm not sure if seventeen-year-old Caroline would have believed me; she was hell-bent on making her mark on this world and taking it by storm, but I would have tried to talk some sense into her.

So there I was looking down the path of the great unknown. I felt like I was on the super scary high dive of life looking into the deep end of an Olympic-size pool. There was no turning back. So I stood up straight, looked right into the dark mysterious path, and decided to be as strong and unbreakable as I knew how to be. I became very, very thin.

THE DECISION

Eating disorders. Some of you may know very little about this topic. Some of you may know more than you would like to admit. Studies indicate that just in the United States, an estimated twenty-eight million Americans will suffer from an eating disorder at some point in their lives.[5] Moreover, eating disorders are the second deadliest mental illness (opioid addiction being the first), resulting in approximately 10,200 deaths a year.[6] And these numbers certainly have not improved over the past several years. Eating disorders are known to thrive in isolation, and the pandemic created quite an isolating atmosphere for most.[7]

It is also important to point out that every year the weight loss industry spends billions of dollars on advertising. Their message is clear. Lose weight and you will feel better. Lose weight and your life will magically improve. And to be honest, as I bought into this mindset and restricted my calorie intake, I did feel better. I did feel more in control of my destiny. Unstoppable in fact. At this point I was what some would call "flirting" with an eating disorder. SlimFast, Weight Watchers, Lean Cuisine—these brands were all the rage. And I began to buy them in bulk! It was a rush to see how little I could eat each day. It felt a little exciting and a little scary. It was a slippery slope. And a complete distraction from the anxiety I had been feeling just a few weeks before.

Excited and scared. That is a good description of where I was at that moment. A senior in high school, I saw my future as one huge enigma. What in the world was I going to do with my life? I was managing my intense anxiety by practicing unhealthy eating. It started with just restriction, but the intensity grew daily. All I knew was that I had a goal, and that goal kept me from thinking about the anxiety of the future.

My goal was to become less.

Pouring my intensity and energy toward this new obsession was insulating me from the unknown. If I controlled "me," then I could at least have some sense of control. These are all thoughts I can communicate now, but of course at the time I had no idea why I was doing what I was doing. I just knew it felt good. And something inside me felt invigorated. It would take a very long time to learn that my new obsession was just a daily grind toward darkness. Little by little I was fanning the flame of anorexia.

I'm not sure how long I stayed in this beginning stage of an eating disorder. A few weeks? A month? But it didn't take long for the intensity to grow. At first I was just skipping dessert, but soon I was skipping breakfast, lunch, and sometimes dinner. An apple, a Lean Cuisine meal, a SlimFast shake, black coffee—there were only a few approved items I would allow into my body. I was becoming addicted to starving.

Some people are more prone to addictive behavior than others. I am one of those people. I like intensity. I like a mission. The mantra "Go big or go home" feels right to me. Well, let me tell you, this new mission was in full swing. I was all in! And this new way of life did seem to soften the anxiety of the future. By rapidly losing weight, I felt like I was the one holding the reins. Little did I know how wrong that was. The control I felt in restricting my food intake was but an illusion. That is the irony with an eating disorder. You start down this path holding the reins, but ever so slowly the reins you once "held" begin to take hold of you. They become handcuffs, holding you hostage. It's the eating disorder with all of the control, not you.

I'm not sure that everyone who treacherously walks down the path of an eating disorder has the same opportunity that I did. I can only tell my story. But I was given a significant moment of clarity one day. This experience is so etched in my memory that I can remember where I was, what was going on around me, and even the sounds and smells of it all. It was an ordinary moment on an ordinary day, but little did I know I would receive a divine message.

School was about to start for me and my two younger brothers. It was late August and it was hot. This was Texas, so late summer meant blazing sunshine and one-hundred-degree-plus temperatures for days on end. Back to school meant that there were new clothes and new backpacks to purchase, endless papers and permission slips for mom to sign. It was a busy time for a family with three teenagers. Activity at our house was always alive and well. But for me this time stood still. I was about to have an encounter with God and one of His angels. He knew what was going on in my heart and mind. His loving-kindness longed to make me aware of the destruction I was running toward. But was I ready to listen?

The August heat made outside activities very difficult. Early morning practices at 7 a.m. for football or cheerleading were a must. This was one of those days. We took our roles as Texas cheerleaders very seriously. Football season was a big deal—this was Texas for crying out loud! Twice a day we would meet at the practice field for cheers and stunts and stretches and exercises; we called these "two-a-days." It was all-consuming. Total commitment was necessary to be on this cheer team. This was my second year of being a varsity cheerleader, so I knew the ropes, the requirements, and the hours necessary to be part of the team. But there was a new priority sneaking into me, a secret one. And on this ordinary weekday morning, I believe an angel was about to make a statement that could change everything.

It was a Tuesday, mid-morning. I was home from the first of two cheer practices that day. The schedule was grueling until football season was over. We were allowed to go home after practice to rest up and take a break from the heat until practice number two began later in the afternoon. I was making my bed. That's when the moment happened. I was kneeling on the soft blue carpet beside my full-size mattress and tucking the sheets into the right side of my bed when I heard the voice.

"You need to tell Mom and Dad. This is getting out of hand."

I heard this voice coming from my right shoulder. It gently whispered this warning during that mundane moment in my bedroom. I knew exactly what this voice was talking about. Of course it was getting out of hand! This new obsession of mine was growing like a raging wildfire! Someone once told me that an obsession is the first thing you think about in the morning and the last thing you think about before you go to sleep. That was definitely where I was. And the intensity was growing. Quickly.

I didn't have much time to contemplate what the first voice had said before I heard the next voice. When I heard the first voice, I knew it was the voice of reason. I knew it was the voice of truth. It felt like a pleading angel, one who knew me and loved me and saw the devastation waiting ahead of me. It was a kind voice, a concerned voice. A careful voice. But there was another voice coming. A darker and meaner voice that spoke more boldly.

A brief lull hung in the air before the second voice emerged. It seemed like I was standing in the middle of these two voices. The first had warned, had spoken truth, had held up a mirror of sorts in order to expose what was going on in my mind and heart. But the second voice was about to steal center stage. The first voice was sweet, but the second voice was crafty. It spoke with an intensity that the first voice didn't possess. The first voice was steady, but the second voice was desperate.

"You can't give up now—you do everything 100 percent! Knock this out of the park like you do everything else!"

There they were. The two voices. The two paths. One led to life. The other to death. And there I was kneeling on the carpet caught in the middle of them both. A scared seventeen-year-old cheerleader with a decision to make. And I made that decision in record time. It only took me a second to decide which road I would continue down. I always cringe when I think about this moment. How could I have chosen the darker path? I knew better! I knew that this dark and conniving voice coming from my left shoulder was a liar. It was so obvious that the first voice wanted life for me. It was the wiser path. It was truth!

But that path didn't solve the internal dilemma I was wrestling with. I didn't want health and safety and wisdom; I was desperate. I wanted to take control of my future, and this darker voice forcefully fanned that flame. The voice of wisdom knew that I didn't have it all figured out. That God was in control. That I was His child in search of answers that only He could give. Deep down I knew that was the path that led to life and peace. But the conniving voice begged me to take matters into my own hands. Screw safety, I wanted control!

It was just a matter of a few seconds. The moments between the first voice and the second voice. I was still there kneeling on the carpet with my fingers still tucking in the sheets. There were people still talking downstairs. A vacuum running in the playroom. Just the sounds of an everyday Tuesday in our busy household of five. The sun was streaming in my pretty bedroom like it always did. The temperature was rising outside while the air conditioning kept our cozy home at seventy degrees. The heated battle raging inside my heart did not match the cool and pretty setting I was in. Normalcy on the outside, a desperate war on the inside. No one would have known what was going on if they had walked past my room that morning. What an ironic picture of peace versus war. And make no mistake about it, what I was getting ready to enter was war.

There is nothing part-time about an eating disorder; it is all or nothing. You either avoid it or you are engulfed in it. There is nothing good or right or wise about it. And yet in that moment I saw that destructive path as the winner. Like I said, in that moment it was as clear as day. Sadly, the dark path wildly outshone the other. Just as I imagine a Las Vegas strip of lights and excitement lure one into the vastness of opportunity and potential jackpots, that dark voice won hands down.

Now let me be clear. I didn't walk slowly toward that dark voice. I ran. I didn't even give the first voice a chance. I didn't thank it or apologize for declining its kind invitation. I dismissed it, pretended I didn't hear it, ignored it like a rude snob. I turned to the dark voice that cunningly grinned at me from my left shoulder. And in one fell swoop I jumped. I had taken that precious moment of clarity and laughed in its face. The decision had been made, and in record time. I went all in. I knew that this performance-driven, successful seventeen-year-old was headed to the top, and no one was going to stop her. "Don't cry for me, you safe and careful guardian angel on my right. You will not save me today," thought the part of me that was already lost in the eating disorder. I smiled a dangerous smile to the dark voice and felt the sick pleasure of the darkness winning. It could have been so different. If I had just known that this path I was getting ready to run down would only hurt and aim to destroy. If I had only listened to truth. But no, maybe two or three seconds passed before I knew I was all in. The fire had been stoked. Just you wait, world, you haven't seen anything yet.

And I leapt with abandon into the ugly mouth of an eating disorder.

"YOU ARE CHUBBY"

Words are powerful.

They can encourage and they can belittle. They can be life-giving, even life-changing, but they can also cut us to our core.

Sometimes I wish this wasn't so true. Careless phrases escape from all of our lips and can wreak havoc. They can hurt. And they often hurt those we love the most. But we are also capable of speaking words that are validating and life-giving. Words that inspire us to be better. Words that encourage others to think more of themselves. I suspect most of us have experienced both kinds. I know I have.

I was born on July 3, 1974, in Dallas, Texas. A birthday I shared with my amazing great-grandfather Robert Walton Bridges. He is kind of a legend in our family. He was a bigwig with Purina in the 1930s. He was even in the Guinness Book of World Records for hitting the longest hole in one with a putter! He was just that kind of guy. He was married to my equally wonderful great-grandmother Elizabeth Rawlings Bridges. We called him Nani and her Noni; weird I know.

They had only one son, my grandfather Bob. My sweet grandmother Teenie, who was Bob's wife, loved to tell me the story of the day I was born. Her narrative began with my mom going into labor on the morning of the third. I did not arrive until much later that afternoon. So Teenie and Bob waited by the phone most of the day until they found out who had joined the family. As soon as they knew it was a pink bundle of joy, they raced over to Nani and Noni's house to share the amazing news. Teenie loved to tell the part about handing Nani a birthday card that afternoon with the words written, "Today you have a new great-granddaughter."

She gave a wonderfully dramatic rendition of his exact expression as he read this card aloud and said with both joy and disbelief, " I have a great-granddaughter? Born on *my* birthday?"

There hadn't been a little girl in our family for several generations. Nani was one of many boys, my grandfather Bob was an only child, and my father was one of two boys. So to receive a great-granddaughter on his actual birthday was a jaw-dropping, Texas-sized big deal!

I loved when Teenie told this story. These words of hers showered me with love. They made me feel so special. They made me feel so celebrated. I never grew tired of hearing her tell it. I knew I was the apple of her eye. You could just tell she cherished the day I arrived in this world.

She would go on to tell of seeing me in the hospital for the first time and noticing the little crease on my left arm below my elbow.

"There you were in the little pink blanket. And I saw that precious little crease on your left arm. Oh how I loved that little crease! I knew you were mine!"

She had a way of making me feel so incredibly unique and valued. I still look at that crease in my arm today and think of Teenie. She had that gift of making people feel special. She lit up the room everywhere she went. She was not only physically beautiful, but her powerful presence was magical. Her words were always intentional. If she loved you, you knew it.

We remember words like these. Words of affirmation. Words that tell us who we are. Defining words like these are usually from people we are very close to. People we look up to. Important people. And my family was and is very important to me. I don't ever remember a time I didn't feel loved growing up. I know this is quite a blessing, really a luxury.

Both my parents and grandparents wanted the best for me. Love and care and support were always present in my childhood. But that doesn't mean I didn't hear words that hurt. Good intentions don't always line up with good results. I know that I too have said things to my children that have hurt them. Of course I didn't mean to. But it happens. To all of us. So I am certainly not here to judge. But words are powerful. And I remember some that stung.

There is a day I remember well. My entire family—Mom, Dad, my two younger brothers, and I—were at the Austin airport early one morning headed to Colorado for our yearly trip. Every summer we flew out west for a week of hiking, fly fishing, horseback riding, and camping. I have wonderful memories of the cool Colorado air and how it was such a respite from the Texas summer and its oppressive heat.

I was sitting next to my dad in the terminal as we waited for our flight. Just the two of us were talking. Plastic blue chairs, large windows at our back. Mom and my brothers were sitting a little bit away from us. I may have been nine or ten. I'm not sure. It was as if he just needed to tell me something. It was a very matter-of-fact phrase he said during our conversation, and it was handed to me like a new title.

"You are chubby."

I can't remember the rest of the chat. I'm sure that wasn't the only thing he said, but it was the only thing I heard. He didn't say it with frustration or disdain. It was just more of a statement. As if he needed to let me know this was just who I was. He handed this title to me with little sign of emotion. I remember knowing that the adjective he had just spoken over me was not a good thing. It stung a little, knowing that women around me were always trying be thin. My mom, my friends' moms, my babysitters, my camp counselors, all of them were always wanting to lose a little weight. I knew that much. And since Dad was a busy doctor, I didn't have much time with him. So the words he spoke felt heavier because of our limited communication at that point in my life. I remember receiving this phrase with obedience, like you would take a vitamin or a pill. No questions. No use arguing about it. Just swallow.

I was a little chubby as a young girl. But when I hit my early teen years, I seemed to grow long and lean overnight. I felt like I woke up one day and suddenly had a different, more acceptable, physique. I didn't change my eating habits. I didn't start exercising. It just happened naturally. And after it happened, I started hearing everywhere I went, "Oh my goodness, Caroline, you look so good!" "Wow, Caroline, what have you been doing? You have changed so much and now look wonderful!"

Geez, how bad did I look before? Though I felt powerful receiving all the praise, questions like this started filling my mind. I now felt like I had a captive audience applauding me for this "dramatic change" that I didn't have one thing to do with. It was confusing.

And then my grandfather Bob noticed. Boy did he ever give me praise! Both Teenie and Bob came to our house to visit fairly often, but I remember this one day Bob just couldn't get over my new appearance.

"Oh Caroline, I can't tell you how good you look!" I remember him telling me that day.

It was sweet. I felt like he really thought I was one heck of a good-looking granddaughter. But in another way, it made me feel a little sad. Did he not think I looked good before? What if something happens and I go back to my old self? I didn't do anything to create this new svelte me, so what if my body decided to go back to its old ways? Will he love me just as much? I felt like I had a new standard. I liked all this affirmation. Especially from my tough marine grandfather who fought in World War II. His words were potent. He loved me, I knew that. And he always had. But these compliments about my appearance were jarring. The performer in me certainly loved a happy audience, and the applause for my physical self was as loud as it had ever been. So the pleasure I felt when I received these compliments was mixed with fear. Was their love for me dependent on how I looked? Did he love me more now? Would the rest of the world now love me more?

Oldest child. Only daughter. Two younger brothers. Beautiful mother. My father a well-respected, successful surgeon. When I was in the outpatient program for eating disorders, it was sort of a joke that I was the "perfect" anorexic. I had all the cards stacked against me, some would say. I was also a teenager in the 80s. Thin was in, and I was well-aware of our diet-crazed society. "A shake for breakfast, a shake for lunch, and a sensible dinner" was the SlimFast mantra, a new drink on the scene that introduced the phrase "meal replacement." This powerful campaign worked.

Everyone knew that girls were supposed to eat less than boys. That certainly was the case in my family. Moms were always on a diet. I have memories of my mom always wanting to lose that last five pounds. She would write me when I was at camp, celebrating that she had lost weight and was trying hard to lose just a little more. Tab was the drink of choice those days. If you are under the age of forty-five, Tab was the precursor to Diet Coke. Google it. It came in a beautiful pink can and was awesome.

I have memories of Mom calling to us kids upstairs, "Boys, your pizza is here! Caroline, I have our dinner ready." She had prepared a healthier alternative for the two of us. Grilled chicken or a piece of broiled fish. Not all the time, but again a memory that was burned into my internal journal. I remember Teenie, who was a tiny little lady, used a small saucer as her dinner plate at times. The rest of us at the dinner table had normal sized plates, but she had a saucer. A little odd? Yes, but remember this precious soul also froze her trash. Whether she intended to or not, her small china saucer at the table was a sign for me to watch my portions. That was what ladies did in my family. It's what ladies everywhere seemed to do. For someone like me, I got the message loud and clear. And I took it to the next level.

Our culture was obsessed with how we looked and what we ate. In the 80s it was all about *fat-free*. Fat-free cookies, desserts, ice cream, and this was when the frozen yogurt sensation arrived on the scene. It was a dream come true for dieters! Eat all the good stuff with none of the guilt! If I had a dime for every time I ate a rock-hard, fat-free, tasteless muffin, I would be a zillionaire.

Have things gotten better with these food obsessions? Maybe. But are we now just as obsessed with things like eating "clean"? It is important to care about what we put in our bodies, but is it the *most* important thing? Each of us has to answer that question. I can tell you that now what I eat is not the most important thing to me, and that is a miracle! It is such freedom knowing that I can eat anything and not be anxious about it.

And what about our body-obsessed culture? Where are we with that? I like seeing that curves are in, not just skin and bones. Thank you, Kardashians. Is strong the new skinny? I hope so. Fit is certainly what I am aiming for. We can't change everyone's mindset, but we can start with us. You and me. Do you believe that your body was made to do more than look a certain way? Like walk, and dance, and serve, and do life with others? Can we at least think of our bodies as something to enjoy rather than something to stress about?

I can now. But I couldn't then. I was convinced chubby was bad and skinny was good. I trained my mind to think all food was a necessary evil. I took daily internal vows never to eat "bad" foods again. Pizza, desserts, French fries, Mexican food—once these were my favorites! But now they had become the enemy. I started to demonize these innate objects and declare war on anything caloric. The voice that easily convinced me to jump into an eating disorder was screaming in my ears. I obeyed its marching orders: "Eat as little as possible. Hide this secret from others. Let no one know what is really going on inside your head. No one must sense the angst, the sadness, the intense hunger." So I did. I charmingly hid from everyone what was really going on inside of me. Remember, I am a great actress.

HOMECOMING QUEEN

It was a *Friday Night Lights* kind of night. My senior year. Late September. I stood in front of a dingy mirror in the poorly lit bathroom of our high school football stadium. Large and grimy, this Texas-sized ladies' room was vacant except for a couple of girls reapplying red lipstick and giving their already big blonde hair an extra dose of hairspray. We were minutes away from walking onto the field, where one of us would be given the highly anticipated crown. Homecoming queen. Excited butterflies may have been what the other girls were feeling, but not me. I was hearing the voice. The mean, hateful voice of my eating disorder that deafened my ears to the cheering crowds of friends and fans that night.

"I am so fat. I am so fat! They are all looking at me right now."

It was all I could hear. It was a lie, of course. I wasn't the least bit fat. I had dwindled down from a perfectly average size seventeen-year-old to a very thin one over the last couple months. I was now caught in the chains of my eating disorder. Ensnared by its darkness and trapped by its lies.

Up until now this book has been easy to write. Some scenes from my past have been easy to recall, like they were patiently waiting below the surface. But the scenes from this time period are different. They have been buried a little deeper. They are darker and more difficult to access. Like they aren't sure they want to be remembered. I am not sure I want to remember them either.

Around this time, I began a new ritual. Daily I began to write a small number on the palm of my left hand. I usually started with the number ten. It was to remind me of the goal, the number of pounds I wanted to lose. It didn't take long for my weight to drop, so I would adjust the number on my palm to nine, and then eight, and then seven. But what never happened was satisfaction. Once I had lost five or six of the initial ten pounds, I would repeat the cycle and write the number ten *again*. A never-ending round of dissatisfaction. It was never enough.

We were a busy household of five. My father the busy surgeon, my mother busy taking care of all of us, and my brothers and I busy with sports and school. Busy, busy, busy. And we all know what can happen when we are busy. Family meals went by the wayside. Family dinners began to be a thing of the past. Practices ran late and everyone was on a different schedule, so skipping dinner or eating a frozen Lean Cuisine meal went under the radar. And that was the way I liked it.

When you see your child become super disciplined, it is hard not to be impressed at first. Parents want their kids to have a mission and go for it. Discipline is a gift. But there is a moment when you know it has gone too far. Too much of a good thing. And then you feel the fear that your child might be dealing with something bigger than them.

And those gut feelings are usually right. My mom knew something was wrong. "Did you eat dinner, Caroline?" my mom would ask. "Yes, I did," was all I answered. She knew. She saw me dwindling away but had no idea what to do about it.

I remember one day during this time a big group of my friends and I all went for a Tex-Mex lunch. My friends were admiring my self-control of not eating the chips and queso set before us. In Texas, chips and queso are a food group. It was a standard. My friends were enjoying themselves having that ultimate appetizer, but not me. I was not about to have one chip. *Not one.*

"Caroline, of course you aren't eating these! You are so good. No wonder you have the best figure," one of the girls said.

I tried to change the subject. I didn't want them to see what was really going on underneath this so called "discipline." If they only knew I longed to be them. They seemed free. I wasn't. It may have looked like I had it all under control. But in reality it was my eating disorder that was controlling me.

What is the difference between disciplined eating and an eating disorder? A lot I think. It's motive. It's your heart. It's the why behind the actions. Why are you choosing to restrict? Is it because you aren't hungry? Good, learn to listen to your body and eat when you are hungry. Or is it because you see that food as too powerful? As something that is bad that you can't handle. That's where I was. Food had become a monster to me.

So I was wearing the shiny crown and holding the beautiful bouquet of long-stemmed red roses. I was standing with my sweet friend and fellow cheerleader Jamie, who had just been named homecoming king, and we walked over to the loud cheering crowd congratulating us from the stands. It was a fairy-tale moment. I only wish I could have enjoyed it.

I reached up into the stands to hug my best friend, Cynda, and I could barely hear her words over the loud noise.

"Can you believe it? You are homecoming queen!"

How I wanted to join her in the sweet excitement she felt for me. She and I knew it was a moment I had always dreamed of. But I just wasn't there. I was too trapped in the cage that held me captive. I didn't want to be thinking only of myself all the time. I wanted to break free from the obsessive thoughts of feeling fat. But I knew it was a lost cause. The exit ramp to a mind of peace wasn't even something I could fathom.

Maybe I have a hard time remembering those few months because I was so hungry. Our high school cafeteria was famous for the freshly baked rolls that came out of the oven at about 10:30 each morning. I dreaded that smell. Before I stopped eating, those rolls were a regular fifteen-cent treat that we all enjoyed, that I enjoyed. But now they were a gateway to disaster. A forbidden food. An absolute no. It is hard to concentrate when you are starving. And there was so much scheming to do. Daily I had to come up with reasons why I couldn't join others for lunch. Or dinner. I spent so much time alone. Me and my thoughts of not eating. Not a happy place to be.

As seniors we were allowed to go off campus for lunch. Most of the time I would drive home to eat an apple and then drive back to school. I was avoiding everyone. All I had to say was that I had left something at home. Or I would stay in the choir room with my apple and Diet Coke, "studying for a test." Isolation. That's what I did well during that time. On the weekends I came up with great excuses as well. "I already ate, guys. I'll just meet y'all after dinner." A lie. But at least it got me out of having to go to a restaurant.

I also have the memories of early morning cheer practice. Or at least getting ready for school after cheer practice. All of us headed to the locker rooms to shower and dress for the day. I would skillfully move to another part of the locker room so no one could see me. I knew I would be found out if so. My ribs had never stuck out like this before. I did get comments from some people. They seemed concerned about how much weight I was losing, but I always had an explanation. I assured them I was fine and that they must be just seeing things. Or that the outfit I had on was deceiving. It was a season of hiding. Hiding the truth of the warfare going on inside of me.

I can see how someone would think it sounds absurd to create this lifestyle of misery. It is totally avoidable, right? I wish I knew myself. But this is the life of addiction. Even though it is lonely and hard and you are hungry all the time, you still feel safe—like you have come into a new, dependable place and you no longer live like the rest of the world does. You envy others who seem to live a life of peace with food and themselves. Someone who can just eat when they are hungry and not constantly obsess over scales and calories. But you don't know how to get to the other side.

I remember my grandfather telling my parents one time, "Why can't you just put food in her mouth and make her chew?" Oh, how we all wished it was that easy. But would that have solved the problem? Was it really about the food I was restricting, or was it more? Oh, it was about much more than food. That is what makes this disorder so hard. It is about control, and fear, and anxiety, and illusions of perfection. Food is just the conduit. The object we have decided to wage war on.

"I wish I could be anorexic for just a little while." I have heard this phrase before. Many times, in fact. And of course, I know what they mean. They want that incredible self-discipline. The ability to say no to the dessert. To the queso. The late-night pizza. But here's the problem. You can't have one without the other. You can't have the eating disorder without the darkness—the harsh voices constantly telling you that you are fat and everyone is talking about how fat you are. You can't have the good without the bad. Self-discipline is good. It's important for a healthy life. But that's not what an eating disorder is. It may start out as self-discipline, but then it moves toward total consumption. It's a slippery slope. You are never satisfied. It is never satisfied. You are never skinny enough.

During those few lonely months, I thought it was still just my secret. But Mom and Dad were about to call me out. And it would be somewhat of a relief. Carrying around an eating disorder at seventeen is a heavy load. You don't really want this burden, but you don't know how to get rid of it. And if you do get rid of it, who are you then? This was hard stuff. Hard to verbalize. To admit to someone else. I can still remember the few people who sat me down and confronted me with their concern. Now that is hard to do. It is risky. You have to be willing to upset the person you are confronting. They may not want to talk to you again. But I remember the few who did the brave thing and voiced their concerns. I won't forget. I saw your courageous love for me. And I felt cared for, even if I denied it. Even if I said I was fine and you were being silly. I knew you loved me. I knew I was not all alone.

Not long after I was crowned homecoming queen, I was woken up early one morning to have a "chat" with my dad. He was done watching me starve myself. I had taken this too far in his mind. I knew he thought this was behavior was ridiculous. "Let me take care of this, I will talk to her," I can just hear him telling my scared mom. He knew I was a bright girl and he was convinced he could talk me out of this stupidity. Or so he thought.

Day by day, lost pound by lost pound, I disappeared more and more into the dark trench that the eating disorder continued to dig. Yes, it was getting out of control, and I was only getting started.

CUT IT OUT

"Caroline. Get up. Come downstairs." I heard my dad's voice in my darkened bedroom.

What? This had never happened. It was an early weekday morning during my senior year. He never woke me up like this. And he certainly never asked me to join him for a pre-dawn talk. Dad wasn't the type to want to chitchat before school. He really wasn't the type to chitchat. It wasn't that we didn't have a good relationship, we got along just fine. But in my family there was a healthy fear of our dad. Especially if he was asking you to get out of bed and follow him. So I didn't argue.

I walked down the stairs and followed him to the study. Neither of us talked on the way down. I had brief moments where I wondered what he was going to say. Being a surgeon, he was used to giving orders. And those orders were always followed. It was one of his specialties. And I was about to get a direct command.

Dad motioned for me to sit down. I sat. He stood. I looked up into his stern eyes. No words. A few moments of this awkward silence. It felt like I was in trouble and was about to be punished. I wasn't nervous. Instead, I found myself intrigued by what he was going to say. What could he say? Did he really have any idea what was going on inside of me? Disdain began to brew in my heart. What in the world did he think he could do for me? I couldn't wait to hear his thoughts.

"Cut it out," he said.

And that was all he said.

I sat motionless. He stood motionless. I knew he meant those three words. He wanted me to cut out this needless behavior that was causing my mom to cry for hours at a time. Surely she had begged him to get involved and say something to me. I knew his thoughts were that "this silly dieting" was unnecessary. He knew I was a rational human being, so he felt certain he could make me aware of this absurd behavior, hence telling me to cut it out. It wasn't an unreasonable request. But he didn't understand. He had no idea what kind of demon I was dealing with.

Silence hung in the air. I had nothing to say. I was undone by how simply he had chosen to handle this. I just sat there stunned. Three words. Three measly words. I was insulted. You could tell that he thought those three pitiful words were somehow going to help. Going to instruct. Going to save me. But those three words backfired. Big time.

"Do you hear me? Cut it out!" he said again.

Disbelief was all I could muster. "Really?" I thought. "I have been fighting a battle with evil and you want me to merely cut it out? I'll show you." The sinister feeling grew. Power. "You think you have power, but actually I do." If he had looked deep into my eyes, he would have seen someone ready to fight. Inside I was amused by his pitiful attempt to stop my efforts. His words fanned the flames of the eating disorder. I would show him. If he wanted me back, he would have to fight harder.

So by this time my secret was out. Mom knew. Dad knew. Teenie and Bob knew too. And they were worried. I couldn't hide it anymore physically. I didn't really care. I wasn't ready to give up my new life, even though it was lonely, hard, dark, and sad. I wanted to stay in that place. I loved knowing what my daily goal was. I had left the anxious world of what my future would look like and instead dug a dark hole into the world of anorexia. I was huddled in miserable darkness and yet charged up with enthusiasm at the same time. Twenty-five years into recovery these words don't make sense. How could I have allowed it to get so bad? And yet I can still remember vividly.

This was fall of my senior year. Mom demanded we all go to therapy. Family therapy. "This ought to be interesting," I thought!

I remember all five of us were expected at our first appointment. We all drove separately: clue number one that this high-achieving family was operating a tad off sync. The therapist was a kind and mild-mannered woman with short blonde hair. Her tidy office was in an old historic home in downtown Austin. It was comfortable and lovely. My mom had done her homework in finding someone who could help us, and this therapist had come highly recommended. I bet she was pricey.

"I would love to learn about your family," she said quietly and calmly to all five of us.

Let me be clear, we all thought this was awkward. But I also thought it was kind of wonderful. My busy family all together in one room to talk about what was wrong with us. With me. I knew Mom wanted this to happen. She needed it to happen. She was desperate to get us back to being a healthy crew.

The therapist did something in that first session that I still think of often. She had a mobile in her office, suspended from the ceiling near a window. You could tell it was less about decoration and more of a tool. She gently pulled one of the wooden objects hanging near the bottom. That one little pull on the lower object affected all the other connected objects. The entire mobile began to move.

"See," she said, "you can't move one piece of the mobile and it not move all of them. This is like a family."

How true this is. Sometimes we don't want it to be true. But it is. Families were designed to work this way. To move this way. It is why we are so affected by our parents, our siblings, our grandparents. Families are a sacred unit. They were God's unique design. They do not ultimately define us, but their influence is undeniable and powerful. A family, made up of many different people, can't help but move together as a unit. If one of us goes down, no one is exempt.

The next therapy session didn't go very well. We all knew we had an appointment that afternoon. Four of us arrived on time, but Dad wasn't there.

"We can't meet until the entire family is here," the kind and soft-spoken therapist said. It was tough love. Wouldn't the four of us get at least something out of this time, we asked? "No," she said. "The family isn't here."

We left her office a little stunned that she really meant what she said. Mom wasn't happy. She later told us that she marched into Dad's office that afternoon and told him unequivocally that if they lost me to this eating disorder she would leave him. Whoa. Dad didn't miss another appointment after that.

In his defense, his absence was caused by an emergency at the hospital where he was serving as the chief of surgery. In fact, I remember seeing whatever issue it was as a headline in the paper the next day. He had a pretty good excuse. Nevertheless, if the family was going to meet for a therapy session, all five of us needed to be present. It was a powerful lesson to me about the role we *all* play in a family.

So my family had a role to play in this. Really? I wasn't sure I bought into that. This was my issue, right? My decision. My path that I chose. So why did they have to be so involved? My brothers had nothing to do with this. Mom and Dad weren't a part of my issues. And yet therapy began to shed some light on my upbringing and my family, and this helped me understand some of my behaviors. For example, later on a doctor said to me that if I had slammed a few more doors and said a few more cusswords I probably wouldn't have been anorexic. Anorexia had become my way of "acting out." I had never really done that before. I was the kind of girl who did the right thing. I was typically compliant. Our family didn't yell or slam doors. Which isn't a bad thing, but conflict happens. Anxiety happens. And emotions need somewhere to go. I had chosen to stuff mine inside, and this eating disorder was like my body screaming out for help.

It wasn't long after dad's intervention that sweet Teenie asked me to come over and talk. When I got to her familiar kitchen for lunch that day, she had sandwich ingredients laid out on her counter for me to see. Fat-free mayonnaise, light wheat bread, turkey, lettuce, and tomato. She had done her homework. She had asked Mom what I would most likely eat. Seeing all the thought she put into that lunch warmed my heart and saddened it at the same time. My family was scared.

We sat down in her bright, pretty dining room together, the room we used for Christmas Eve and Thanksgiving. She looked at me with heavy and concerned eyes. "I know this is my fault, Caroline," she said. What? I couldn't believe she was saying that! "No, Teenie it's not," I tried to assure her. Sure, she had emphasized portion control and worked hard at staying thin, but I was not going to let Teenie think she caused this. This sweet confession she was making was so precious to me. And though she didn't cause it, she recognized that her behavior and attitude around the importance of being thin could not have helped.

Looking back, I see that special lunch with Teenie as a real milestone. Her humility and honesty in telling me she was sorry did not solve the problem, but it was still powerful. She wasn't defensive. She didn't try to tell me that she did everything she could to prevent this. I still see that sacred lunch as a very selfless act. It is a lesson for all of us. A lesson for me even now. Taking risks like that is brave. And offering herself up like that was monumental to me. It was love.

The rest of my senior year of high school, I worked with a therapist, saw a nutritionist, and continued to go through the motions of getting better. Still, I wasn't particularly committed to recovery; I just wasn't sure how badly I wanted to be anorexic. Like I had mentioned, it was isolating, dark, and I was so hungry, so I wasn't sure how bad of an idea it was to get better. I was in a kind of no-man's-land.

And then something tragic happened within our circle of friends. Our dear and beautiful friend Kristen died in a car accident over spring break. She was in the back seat of the car, riding with some other friends of mine. It was gut-wrenching. She was in a coma for about a week until she went home to heaven. We all grieved so hard together. It was awful, and we were faced with the fragility of life. Our precious friend left this earth so soon, and our already tight friend group mourned together for the remainder of the year. For a while I began to think that the restricted eating was so silly, so selfish, so needless. I allowed myself to eat the queso, to be with everyone at meals, and to celebrate our graduation from high school with party after party and cake after cake. I'm sure I seemed fine. Like I had moved on from that bad habit. Like I had wised up and decided that an eating disorder was wasting time and energy. I gained some weight back. I looked normal again. But I had never really dealt with the disorder. I just stuffed it down for a while.

Then it was the summer before college, and the feelings of anxiety danced back into my head and heart. Teenie and Bob took me to England for a graduation trip. I had a lot of time to myself on that trip, and I remember thinking that I needed to get it together. "I'm about to go to college. It's time to shape things up," I remember thinking. The extreme food restriction started again. I knew the drill. I knew where I was going to college, which was such a relief. But now I had to make my mark there. I had a whole new audience ready and waiting for me! I wanted to present the best me possible. And I knew exactly what to do.

WHO IS ON YOUR THRONE?

College. I had made it. This was what I was so worried about? There I was in Nashville Tennessee, thousands of miles away from my home state of Texas. And I have to say, it really was awesome. The feeling of independence was incredible. I was meeting so many new and interesting people. They just kept coming! Smart, kind, fun, great people. I was studying communications, but I was spending more time actually talking with people rather than learing how to actually communicate with them. One afternoon I remember racing home to my dorm room to begin a written list of all the new friends I was meeting and making. I didn't want to forget any of their names! It really was such an exciting time.

I had collaborated with my cute new roommate, Virginia, over the summer to make sure our dorm room would be adorable. A microwave, a television, a mini fridge, matching comforters—we brought all of these items to make our tiny living quarters feel more like home. We had mutual friends who matched us up. She was a great girl who was kind, super smart, and enjoyable to be around. I was relieved and thankful to find out that Virginia didn't have an unhealthy relationship with food. Could she sense that I did? Did she know that I had packed up my anorexia and brought it with me to the room? I was able to hide this for a while. But ultimately, I was found out, even by my sweet roomie.

My memories of those first few months of college are honestly great. I was still very deliberate about restricting my food intake and was living within the harsh confines of an eating disorder. But for some reason I don't remember the start of freshman year as a dark time. I was with a new group of people who knew nothing else but "small Caroline." In the new environment I didn't have the questions and concerns to deal with like I did back at home. Was it a new audience that made that time feel lighter? You bet it was! I had a new stage, and it was invigorating.

But make no mistake, the hard-core food restriction had come to a sharp climax. Constant hunger was a part of my everyday life. The summer before college I had been restricting my food intake and obsessing over losing weight, and I didn't lose any steam once I arrived at college. I woke up every morning thinking about what I wasn't going to eat, and I went to bed thinking about the short list of foods I had allowed myself to eat. The *yes* list of foods was extremely short: apples, frozen yogurt, bagels, certain diet cereals, Diet Coke, and black coffee. If it had zero grams of fat, there was no guilt. That was what I cared about. My goal was zero grams of fat, no more than about 800 calories a day, and a lot of caffeine.

During this time there were no family dinners to miss. No one was looking to see what I ate. I loved this sense of freedom. And lots of other people around me seemed to have issues with food as well. I saw many girls much thinner than I was. Many were exercising excessively too: running, walking, working out for hours at a time. The lifestyles of restricted eating and excessive exercise were not just normal, they seemed desirable. This was a university filled with type A students. So many of us were there wanting to be the *best*. I fit in just fine.

I can see how someone might ask, "Can you really be genuinely happy and have an eating disorder at the same time?" The truth is that yes, I have wonderful memories of that year. I really do remember feeling so happy. I was forming many real friendships, people who I am still very close to today. I was creating a new life for myself, and I think the key word here is *new*. These people were just beginning to know me, so I could be whomever I wanted to be. I don't remember feeling depressed. Or lonely. Or anxious. How can you live with such a detrimental addiction and still be content? I don't know. It is just what I remember.

But I also remember what it felt like when I returned home to Austin for the first time over Thanksgiving break freshman year. The moment my plane touched down, it was as if the reality of my eating disorder came into clear focus. Immediately I knew I was going to be found out. I knew my family would see the effects of anorexia the second I walked off that plane. I had lost more weight since I had gone to college. When my family hugged my bony shoulders, I knew the gravity of my eating disorder would be exposed. I was trapped in this darkness, perhaps more than ever. I knew I was not in a healthy place. And just the idea of facing my family brought all of that into focus.

On campus I felt great. Coming home was a different story.

———————————

You have to understand that even though I knew I was doing something wrong, I still very much believed in God and wanted Him first in my life. An eating disorder wasn't *that* wrong, was it? It wasn't like I was doing terrible things like getting drunk and shacking up with boys . . . or was this lifestyle actually worse?

Sin is not fun to talk about, and our culture has mastered not bringing it up. But that was what my lifestyle of extreme restriction was. I was trapped in sin. I had allowed something else to be my god. And the God of the universe doesn't like to share His title with anyone or anything. That's just who He is. He allows us to choose our own path; we are not robots. But He also allows us to experience the consequences of our decisions. Choosing an eating disorder over Him was just a "secret" sin at first. Nothing too bad, for crying out loud, look at how celebrated you are when you are extra thin! People are so impressed! And look at all the other people out there doing much worse things. Surely this was not *that* bad. But God had warned me about turning from Him that morning while making my bed senior year in high school, and I had chosen to turn the other way. I'm so thankful that God doesn't hold a grudge. He never stopped pursuing me even when I ran. A parent keeps looking for their child, and I was and am His child. He never stopped running after me.

So even as I was battling a dark addiction, I arrived to campus knowing my faith was very important to me. I was so excited to meet so many friends who felt the same way. I became involved with an on-campus ministry and met so many like-minded people. I started to attend a Bible study for freshman that really rocked my world. I ate it up! I had always loved God and felt His presence in my life, but learning who Jesus really was changed everything for me. I felt like my mind was finally catching up with my heart. I remember racing home to my dorm room after that weekly Bible study to call my mom. Bible studies had always been so important to her, and I was so excited to tell her all that I was learning.

On Sundays, a big group of us from the Bible study group would drive thirty minutes south to attend church. It was wonderfully casual and held hundreds of people in its bright and cheery sanctuary. I had grown up in a formal Episcopal church, so this laid-back worship service without organs or much formality felt different and new.

One Sunday morning I heard a sermon that completely challenged me. I have heard lots of sermons in my lifetime, but God used this one to speak directly to me. You know those moments when you feel like there should be a huge, bright spotlight on you during the service? That the speaker or pastor is speaking *only* to you? That is what this moment was like. Pastor Scotty asked a question that God used to expose what was going on in my heart, the crux of the issue with my eating disorder.

I remember sitting in a windowsill on the right side of the church. The service was standing room only as usual. Pastor Scotty spoke to the congregation so personally, like we were all in his living room, creating an even more relaxed environment for all of us in attendance. That morning he spoke about how we are all born with a throne in our heart. No one is exempt. We all worship something. The question is *who* is on your throne? Is it the rightful King of Kings? Or is it something else? Immediately I felt found out. Like he was looking straight at me!

I knew God was the rightful king and was worthy to be sitting on the throne; I knew it without a doubt. But I also knew that if I was honest with myself, I had let another god take over my heart's throne. I believed that God was in control of the universe, but I was not allowing Him to be in control of my life. I knew it was wrong and ugly, but I didn't know what to do about it.

Who was sitting on the throne of my heart? It looked like the "holy" red plastic scale from Target with bright yellow numbers that I kept hidden in my dorm room closet. I bowed down to that false god several times a day, as I would race home to weigh myself when no one was looking. When I was all alone in our little dorm room, that scale told me if I was good or not. It told me my worth. I let its voice dictate my every move.

"Good job, Caroline, I knew you could do it," if the number was less than the day before.

But, "Well, look what you did now, you are a failure!" if the number was not what I wanted it to be.

That scale was the one who really had control of my life. I had to face it. I knew this little *g* god was ridiculous, but in that moment of clarity I knew the answer to Scotty's question. And I knew it was wrong. I really did want the real God to be on my throne, but I knew the ugly truth. And I didn't have the slightest idea what to do about it.

DR. WILLEFORD

My freshman year in college was over. I had planned a fantastic summer for myself, or so I thought. I had interviewed to be a counselor at a Christian camp in Missouri, and I had gotten the coveted job! But when I returned home to Austin, it was evident to my parents that they needed to intervene. I had lost more weight, and they decided that a plan of action was desperately needed. I argued that I had gotten this great opportunity to be a camp counselor and had a responsibility to do it! But they gave me no choice.

"Caroline will not be coming this summer after all," my mom said into the telephone to the person who would have been my supervisor. I eavesdropped through the bedroom wall with my mouth on the ground. I couldn't believe it. My parents rarely said no; they never really had to. I had never been a wild child. I was usually doing such good things, sometimes too many good things. But now they emphatically said, "You are not going." They weren't buying my empty words that I was going to be just fine. I didn't dare let them see this, but I was impressed with their resolve. And was that a tinge of relief I was feeling?

"We think this is what is wrong with Caroline," my grandfather Bob said to my mom.

He had driven over to our house that morning to hand deliver a VHS tape. He and Teenie had taped the *ABC Primetime* special that had aired just the night before, May 6, 1993. It was a documentary about the well-known actress Tracy Gold and her very public eating disorder. Tracy starred in the popular family television series *Growing Pains*. She had developed anorexia while filming the show, and audiences watched with shock as she dwindled away before their eyes. The documentary was a powerful piece.

I had seen previews for the documentary and was terrified that it would start all sorts of conversations in my family. It did. This secret life of mine was being dragged into the limelight. I once again felt like God was just not leaving me alone. He was even working through television to push me into recovery! My parents knew about my eating disorder before my grandfather handed the recording to them, but it was just more evidence that they needed to act to save me from my eating disorder. Really to save me from myself.

"We know, Bob," Mom replied. We all knew. It was just a matter of what we needed to do next.

I knew deep down that this life I was living was neither healthy nor sustainable, but I had no idea what to do about it. It controlled my daily decisions. It was the first thing I thought about when I woke up and the last thing I thought about when I went to bed. It was my addiction. It was my drug. It was just who I had become. I knew it was wrong, but I couldn't imagine life without it. Who was I without it? Did I even know that person anymore?

No one thinks well in a crisis. Your mind is spinning. You find yourself starting to question everything. Decisions are murky. So it is very advisable to have someone in charge, someone who can think rationally. Someone who is an expert in that field and knows what to expect. Especially when you are in a health crisis, you need to pick your medical team and trust them. That is what I would suggest to anyone going through something like this. And that summer it was Dr. Willeford who came into our world and took the reins.

A few days after I returned home from college, my parents made some phone calls. They must have been relieved to find out that our good family friend Dr. George Willeford was *the* doctor in town to talk to about eating disorders. He showed up in our living room just a few hours later. I didn't yet know him, but he and his wife were good friends with Teenie and Bob. He seemed to know my whole family when he walked in our front door. He knew my dad as a fellow physician in town, he knew my mom, and soon I would grow to know and love him. He had a casual yet commanding presence about him. Tall, graying hair, bright and kind blue eyes, Dr. Willeford looked like the handsome grandfather that you would instantly want to chat with. His words seemed to ring throughout the house when he told all of us,

"I'll take it from here."

You could hear an almost audible sigh from my parents, if not from me as well. It was a relief to know we weren't expected to know what to do. How could we? As a renown psychiatrist in Austin, Dr. Willeford had been instrumental in creating a center for eating disorders at one of Austin's local hospitals. And here he was standing in our living room telling us he would now be our leader. Our coach. It was a critical moment in what would be the beginning of my recovery.

I still remember what it felt like as he stood there with us that afternoon. His voice was quintessential Texas, and his calm countenance was comforting. He took a tough situation and made us feel at ease. He knew girls like me, lots of them. And he told me that I was going to get better. I was skeptical, of course. What did he really know about this prison I was in? Maybe a whole lot.

I was to go to the hospital the next day to learn what my schedule would be. I was going to be an outpatient at the program that Dr. Willeford was so instrumental in starting. Outpatient. That was the category I was placed in. To me that meant I wasn't sick enough to be admitted to the hospital. I only heard that I wasn't anorexic enough. I felt cheated by this disease that had taken over my body.

"Give me just a couple weeks, and I will make sure I am bad enough to be an inpatient," I thought.

In fact, I might have even said this out loud.

"Surely I can't start recovery if I haven't gotten to the point where my life is really in danger. That means there is still work to do. I need to get worse before I can get better. Right? If I don't need to be admitted to the hospital, then why do I need to go at all? Apparently my health is not even in danger! See? I told you all that I was fine!"

Yes, these were my thoughts. I remember them like it was yesterday. I wanted to be the *best* anorexic, and I was just told by my doctor that I was not bad enough. Outpatient meant one thing to me: I had failed miserably. This was the dialogue going on in my head. "Please let me just do what I do a little bit longer, and then I will be ready to lay it down."

Do you know what it means to be the best at an eating disorder? Dying. Winning means you have lost your life to it. But I couldn't see that at the time. I just knew that my plans were derailed and others were taking over for me. My whole goal was to have ultimate control, and I was losing control. Anorexia is the epitome of self-control, right? Wrong. I was totally out of control, and I knew it. So a tiny part of me was thankful. Thankful that Dr. Willeford was in charge.

Thankful that it was no longer my parents' job to talk sense into me. They couldn't do it. My friends couldn't do it. This wasn't about reasoning me out of something. There was nothing reasonable about me or my thoughts or my eating disorder anymore.

As people tried to support me they often said they just wanted me to be healthy. If I had a dime for every time someone said that! I knew they meant for their words to be encouraging, but they just weren't. For me, healthy meant blah. Average. Meh. Same as everyone else. I wanted to be exceptional! Better than just boring old healthy!

Now, I know, these inner thoughts seem ridiculous. Healthy is great! It should be what we hope for our bodies, and of course no one meant for that word to backfire. But I can just tell you that it wasn't helpful. In fact, there really wasn't anything anyone said that was helpful. The only words I remember being helpful were when someone said they were concerned.

"Caroline, I'm worried about you. You have gotten so thin."

I told them there was nothing to be worried about and I was fine, but deep down I was touched. I guess the takeaway is that our words are not as important as our actions. The person you are talking to won't remember what you said. But they will remember that you cared. Isn't this true in all of life? You are more than likely *not* going to talk someone out of an addiction, but you can show them love.

I reported for duty at St. David's outpatient program the next day. Scared, a little ashamed, mad, and partly relieved. What a mixture of emotions. What was this going to be like? What would they tell me that I didn't already know? "I am not going to gain weight," I thought. "It will kill me. I have worked so hard. Skipped so many meals. Endured so many hunger pains. Pretended like nothing was wrong." I remembered the Thanksgiving of my senior year in high school, having an apple on my plate as my only entree. One lousy apple. No turkey, no dressing, no sweet potato casserole. This was who I had become in my family. I was the one who didn't eat the queso, for crying out loud! But I also knew that this life wasn't sustainable.

I was getting ready to meet many like me. And the experts who ran the program were skilled at their jobs. I wouldn't be able to get away with my shenanigans anymore. It was like they had x-ray vision. They saw the shackles we were living with, and they skillfully and lovingly tried to hand us the keys to free ourselves. Would we take them? Would we believe that there was a better life waiting for us outside of these prison walls? Would I believe it? Only time would tell.

WHAT'S THE DEAL
WITH THE MUSTARD?

It was the summer of 1993. One year of college under my belt, and here I was reporting to an outpatient hospital program for a mental health disorder. What? How was this even happening? This was not something I was broadcasting. I was not ready for people to know this was where I would be spending my summer break. This was embarrassing! Did I even need to be here? These were all thoughts I had as I walked into the program doors for the first time.

I must have thought that everyone would look the same in the program, but gosh was I wrong. Underweight, overweight, old, young, black, white. Eating disorders do not discriminate. Binge eating, bulimia, anorexia—each issue was as unique as the person carrying the load.

There was one girl who was about the same age as me. She was outpatient as well. I thought she looked thinner than me. She thought I looked thinner than her. Typical anorexic behavior. So much comparison, and so much of it not based on reality. When I looked in the mirror, I really did see something terrible. I saw someone about a hundred pounds overweight. It is hard to describe, but what we see is not what others see. The darkness of the disorder had stolen my ability to see the true image in the mirror.

Another young girl I remember was so thin you thought she might die right there in front of you. Interesting that I could still see others' sickness, just not my own. She was an inpatient. Around my age, short blonde hair, really quiet and nice. She was so emaciated. It was scary to see her body so deprived of life. Her thighs were about the size of my arms. Didn't she see that she needed to start eating? Surely she couldn't live like that. I'm not sure she did.

There was another woman there in her midthirties and overweight. "What's wrong with her?" I wondered. Obviously she wasn't deathly afraid of food like I was. Or was she? I had so much to learn. We all had issues with food. With control. No one was better than another. There were other ladies in the group that looked completely normal. Many of them suffered from bulimia. They were anything but healthy. Eating and then not getting rid of the food was their daily, maybe even hourly, challenge.

We usually met as a group at least once a day. We sat together, ten to fifteen women, in a big circle of couches and chairs. We were there to check in, to share what was going on with all of us. Who was willing to share their triggers that day? Their feelings? Renee, the skilled counselor, would go around and kindly ask us how we were. Some days there were long minutes of uncomfortable silence and stone-cold faces. Other days there were tears and shouting and honesty. Those days were hard but good. It seemed to me Renee had the hardest job in America.

After the group meeting we had the dreaded evening group meal. Outpatient and inpatient participation was required. It was a long walk from our area of the hospital to the main cafeteria. I lowered my head along the way to ensure my anonymity. I prayed that I wouldn't see anyone I knew on that early evening pilgrimage. What would they possibly think of me if I was found out? Wasn't this something I should be ashamed of? There's no telling what they would say about my nightly dinners with this cast of characters. I still cared so much about the part I was playing. What others thought of me. I mean, I was the one who had it all together, right? These were humbling circumstances. Beautiful and much needed, humbling circumstances.

Our least favorite activity of the day was eating. We awkwardly filed into the cafeteria line together to make our food selections. We chattered nervously, a bunch of frightened, struggling ladies standing in line considering what to put on our plates. A protein, a starch, a vegetable. Ugh! It didn't matter what it tasted like, none of the food looked appealing to me. There were always a few counselors mixed in the line to encourage us and hold us accountable. Talk about pressure! My inner anorexic goal was to get the least amount of food without getting in trouble. God forbid you got more food than another patient. So much comparing going on! Replaying this scene in my mind still makes me cringe.

In the beginning I was surprised they didn't split up the patients. The anorexics at one table and everyone else at another. At least bulimics and overeaters can eat the food, right? Aren't we different? Aren't we at least a little better, since we don't overeat? I soon learned that was wrong. We were all controlled by food. Some of us were starving ourselves and some were stuffing ourselves, but the root of the problem was our eating disorder. We had all been found out and were facing our addictions. It wasn't pretty. But looking back, it was a beautiful table of hope. Of struggle. A picture of people working through the complexities of life together. That table was the great equalizer. We all needed help with the everyday task of eating so we could stay alive.

After going through the line, our group would trudge over to the long plastic table to endure the hardest part of the day: eating. I usually chose a baked potato, a dry chicken breast, and an iceberg salad with no dressing. Sounds delicious, doesn't it? There was nothing fancy or lovely about it. The counselors joined us at the table to assist during this mealtime extravaganza. They were trained to look for struggle. This happened often. They would come whisper in our ear the kind but embarrassing words, "How can I help you right now?" It only happened to me once. I was being ultra-picky that night and not eating my plain baked potato; I was just cutting it up but not actually putting it in my mouth and chewing. Sawing your knife and fork back and forth for minutes at a time was a popular pastime. But the counselors were trained to watch for things like that. And patients were always found out.

I remember a specific awkard moment when a table mate of mine exposed one of our anorexic "tricks." Most people who are anorexic know exactly how many calories and fat grams are in *everything*. But let me tell you about a magic edible item that contains none of them: mustard. Zero calories, zero fat, lots of flavor. We loved us some mustard. This bright yellow condiment became an obsession for all the anorexics at the table. We started adding mustard to all our entrees, no matter what they were. You were having chicken? Add mustard. Vegetables? Mustard was the perfect dipping sauce. We couldn't get enough of it! That was until we were so rudely exposed.

"What is the deal with the mustard?" our bulimic friend blurted out one night during the group meal, loud enough for everyone to hear.

Uncomfortable silence. The anorexics froze. Did she just say that? There was an unwritten rule around here: don't mess with our odd eating habits. This girl just broke the rule. We felt betrayed. This was our deal—not hers! It was our coping mechanism, and she had just ruined it for all of us. "Okay guys, let's cool it with the mustard," one of the counselors said. I sat there feeling exposed and silly at the same time. We were hoping that mustard would hide what was really going on in our struggling little hearts and minds. And we were coming up with games to still feel in control. We were desperate for control. We were playing charades with ourselves and others, but it turned out no one else was buying it.

I can recall these feelings and memories so easily and yet they are so foreign to me now. It saddens me to remember how I once saw mustard as a way to avoid the problem. The me who was not yet ready to relinquish control. Who feared what life would become if I gave in to the experts around me and laid down the addiction. The sickness. To trust them and move toward recovery. It was so scary. I was just clinging to what I knew, but I also knew I was a ticking time bomb.

If you are one of those people sitting at the table of an eating disorder, please hear me! It will not happen overnight, but you can be free of this addiction. I know it is possible. I know it is possible because I never ever thought I would live without the imprisonment of an eating disorder, but I am free now! I want you to be free too. Life is so much better on this side!

The mealtimes were hard to forget, but they were just one part of that summer's treatment. I was required to attend group meetings, one-on-one meetings with therapists, weigh-ins, vital sign checks,

meetings with nutritionists, and one-on-one meetings with Dr. Willeford. One individual meeting I specifically remember. Doctors, nutritionists, and counselors all gathered together to talk about my recovery. Even my parents were there, all of us sitting in one big circle. I
remember I still wrestled with the idea of the severity of my problem.
Because I was not an inpatient, I believed I was not that bad. Maybe
I didn't really have a big enough problem, maybe we were making a
big deal out of nothing.

Dr. Willeford picked up on this dangerous sentiment of mine and
said, in front of everyone, "Caroline, I feel like you are still question-
ing if you are anorexic. You are. We all know you are anorexic. But
we know you will get better. One day you will not have this eating
disorder. You will get better."

If you had been in my head that moment, you would have heard
the resounding statement, "No way!" I remember sitting there looking
at this team of experts with disbelief. They were all looking at me and
nodding in agreement with Dr. Willeford. Encouraging me. They all
seemed so sure of his optimistic statement. But inside I still believed
that I would never be able to live without this cage around me. I just
couldn't imagine it. I trusted Dr. Willeford and knew that he spoke
with assurance and experience in the world of eating disorders, but I
knew that he was wrong. I just couldn't see it. I don't think you can
hear the truth when you are living in a prison.

But that wise public statement he made in front of my parents,
therapists, nutritionists—everyone I was working with—was the dec-
laration I needed to hear. Remember, words are powerful. And his
words validated me. I needed to know that what I was experiencing
was the real thing. Even though I didn't need to be on a feeding tube,
I was still very sick. That realization was a turning point for me. It was
a moment of acceptance. I was supposed to be there.

Here's how change happens: Step by step, day by day, hour by hour. One decision at a time. One step at a time. Now let me be clear, I didn't decide that day that I was going to get better. That was still out of the question in my mind. But I did hear Dr. Willeford tell me that it was possible. And even though it sounded unimaginable, the seed was planted of a life without an eating disorder. What would that even be like? You mean one day this might not rule my every thought?

I spent the whole summer in outpatient treatment. At the end there was a graduation where we were asked to speak publicly about what we had learned and what we were taking away from the experience. They asked us to share a song, something that helped explain how we felt about recovering. I played one about God and how He always loved me. I knew He wanted me to get better. I knew that living in anorexia was a dead-end road. On a scale from 1 to 10, I would say my fervor to get better was about a 6.5. I wanted to walk down the road of recovery, kinda.

The program had given me the tools to live a life free of addiction, but it was still up to me to walk down the path of recovery. What they were asking all of us to do was trust. It felt like being blindfolded while the people around you told you what to do and where to go. I couldn't see a thing. That was what recovery was like at first. It was hard. I had to rely on what others said more than what felt right. I had new healthy habits and meal plans to follow. I had memorized the serenity prayer, the golden rule of recovery, and I knew it was true and good and worthy of pursuing. I had a beautiful, framed version of the prayer that I brought with me to college sophomore year. But there is a big difference between knowing something and doing something. Would I merely recite the serenity prayer, or would I act on it? God only knew, and He knew I needed more convincing.

THE SERENITY PRAYER

God, grant me the serenity to accept the things I
cannot change,
Courage to change the things I can,
And the wisdom to know the difference.

RECOVERY ROAD

The word *sophomore* is derived from the Greek word *sophos*, which means "clever" or "wise," and the word *moros*, which means "foolish."[8] In essence, a sophomore is a wise fool! How appropriate this word was to describe me as I headed back to college after my summer in recovery. I had been accumulating wisdom that summer, but I wasn't great at practicing what I had learned. But I was trying. And that was something.

I showed up for sophomore year with a new mindset. The framed serenity prayer was hanging by the door in my small dorm room. I hung it there as a daily reminder. I needed to remember that this was my new hopeful life. My good friends knew what I had been working on that summer. They knew I was coming back to school with a decision to live differently. But remember, the challenging and competitive university I attended attracted type A personalities. Smart, disciplined, high-achieving ladies everywhere meant there were a lot of girls who struggled with eating disorders. Excessive exercising, obsessing over fat grams, and restricting food were the norm. I felt slightly alone in my new attempt to live a life free of food and body issues. I continued to see girls run for hours at a time who were stick thin. I saw girls eating only frozen yogurt and pretzels for dinner. I thought, "Wait, I thought we were cutting that stuff out?" Just because you get better doesn't mean everyone else will.

I want to emphasize how hard it is to see others not living in recovery when you are struggling to stay on the right path. If I gave up that destructive behavior, surely everyone else should as well, right? Unfortunately the world doesn't work that way. It is a frustrating feeling, to think that others don't yet know the advantages of letting go. Or are you also a tad bit jealous that they can get away with it while you can't? It's okay to be honest about the struggle of laying down an addiction. Remember, there are a lot of things about addiction that feel good. The drive, the intensity, the secrecy, the feeling of power and control. It takes time to understand that the power you felt in addiction was not real. It takes time and patience to believe that the real power comes from being free of it.

I did have a good friend who seemed free of eating and body issues, so I asked her if she would hold me accountable. I asked her if we could regularly eat lunch together. Thankfully she enthusiastically agreed to be this person for me! I gave her the freedom to question me if she thought I was making poor choices. I still think about what a gift it was to have her by my side. She was willing to be my personal lunch buddy and accountability partner when I was in need. I think most of my friends were proud of my attempts to leave my unhealthy lifestyle. They certainly wanted to be encouraging. Not all of them knew the struggle I had lived with the year before, but they were glad to see that I was better.

That year I longed for community outside of my college life. I missed families. I missed seeing children. I missed seeing day-to-day normalcy. I missed being part of a church where people really knew me. One night at the local Mexican spot, I overheard a new friend saying she was going to work with the youth group at a local church, and I blurted out, "I want to do that too!" I was almost surprised by how quickly I was committing to this church ministry that I knew nothing about. It was as if the Holy Spirit had whispered to me, "Say yes to this." It could also have been the margarita I'd just had. Regardless, it was an awesome decision, and I became super involved in that church and its youth program. Soon I was teaching Sunday school and Bible studies for teenagers and even leading worship. The kids were just a few years younger than me, so I was hardly their superior, but I loved getting to know them. I began going to their football games, attending their plays, and even hanging out with their families—all such good opportunities for healthy relationships, which I was longing for. Friends from that church would eventually introduce me to my now husband. Making that decision to step outside of my college bubble and connect to that church community was a life-giving, life-changing decision and one I am forever thankful for.

I believe getting outside of yourself is imperative for authentic recovery. Your world needs to get bigger. My world needed to get bigger. Remember how I said that one of the gifts of an eating disorder is that you are capable of great things? Well, once the eating disorder is gone, you need to replace the bad things with new good things. It takes a lot of time and energy and willpower to be anorexic. But the energy and willpower and discipline are all still there when the anorexia is over, so you must find new interests and hobbies to pour that energy into. This can actually be an exciting part of recovery, to know that you are capable of doing great things!

I stayed involved with the college ministry RUF during sophomore year, learning more about God and His Word. Our leader, Paige, started teaching a Bible study in her home, which I began regularly attending. I couldn't get enough of her dynamic and fast-paced teaching and wise story telling. Most Monday nights a group of about thirty girls would gather around her living room and listen to her teaching straight from the Word of God. Would you believe she is still my Bible teacher today? I am so grateful that the Lord allowed me to be under her gifted teaching then and even now!

Back then Paige and I would occasionally have lunch together on campus. When we would meet up in the cafeteria to choose our entrees, I remember her wisely saying, "I'll have what you are having." Wow, I thought. How can she be so trusting? What if I wanted a cheeseburger and fries or a big greasy slice of pizza? Would she be okay with that? I longed for that kind of relaxed attitude about food. I wasn't there yet. I was still picky about what I would eat. It was very important to me that what I ate was healthy and low-fat. Not a bad thing. But what a gift it is that now I can say those same words, "Just order me something." Each time I say that phrase to a friend I am meeting for lunch I smile knowing that I have come a long way! It's a sentence I commonly text to the person I am meeting if I am running late for a meal. I really do say it honestly and easily. I bask in the freedom I can now experience. But back then that mindset seemed hard to imagine.

The truth is, I was doing okay sophomore year. My parents insisted that I find a therapist I could see on a weekly basis. She and I worked to unpack the feelings I was having while trying to let go of the harsh rituals of anorexia. I would make the thirty-minute trek on the highway to see her each week. I was still taking Prozac, something that was required of each patient in the eating disorder program I had attended. And I am glad it was. Prozac allowed me to feel calmer and less structured. Kind of like a chill pill. When I decided to stop taking the Prozac later in the year, I noticed a big difference. I found myself exercising more, and I was more concerned about what I ate. I also found my room was a mess! "Have I really not been making my bed all semester?" I thought. "Time to get this place tidied up," I pledged to myself. Interesting, right? In hindsight I was not far enough along in my recovery to stop taking the meds. My brain still needed to heal.

The good news was that I was finally living without an active, horrific eating disorder. Praise the Lord! I wasn't obsessing over it every waking moment, and that was in itself a miracle. I had gotten rid of the scale I kept hidden in my closet freshman year, and I was able to enjoy a meal with friends. I knew there were remnants of this illness still hidden in my heart, but I was doing the best I could.

Sophomore year I was enjoying school, loving my friends, and finding out who I was as a student and as a person. I began to intern at an important music company that summer. I was enjoying the music business in Nashville, singing more at my new church, and even considering a career in music.

It had been my plan all along to study abroad during the spring semester of my junior year. Spain was a place I had always hoped to experience. I just knew it would be incredible to live in Madrid, take classes, and galivant around Europe on the long weekends with fellow classmates. I had an appointment with Dr. Willeford just before I left. He said, "Live a little! Gain some weight! Drink the beer and eat the tapas!"

"Does he even know me?" I thought. I wasn't quite ready for that. I certainly didn't want to gain weight. Was this trip going to be a disaster? I started to get nervous.

January of my junior year I packed up my things and headed to Spain for the semester. My roommate, Cate, and I nervously introduced ourselves to our new señora, Marite. We would be living in her modest apartment for the next five months, and she would serve as both house mom and Spanish chef extraordinaire. She was a darling little lady with amazing homemaking skills. She cooked and cleaned like no one I had ever seen before! When discussing the upcoming menus, my roommate told her she was a vegetarian. Sounds good to me, I thought! I told her I was as well. I figured it would be less caloric to eat only veggies, as I was already fearing the Spanish cuisine, known for its greasy meats and heavy tapas.

Marite had been hosting American girls like us for years. She was a devout Catholic and attended daily mass, something I joined her in doing from time to time. But as the weeks went on, I found the perks of living abroad were not exactly my cup of tea.

First, I quickly realized that I wasn't that great at Spanish. In fact, I was 100 percent the worst student in the class. Second, no surprise to me, I really didn't love indulging in Spanish food and wine and all-night partying, which are kind of the reasons you go to Spain. I wouldn't say I was the ideal foreign exchange student. I was determined to not gain weight while I was there. I was anxious that the language did not come as easily to me as some other classmates, and I was homesick. Really homesick.

And what does Caroline do when she feels anxious? Well, I think we know the answer to that. Why not? It worked before. I refused to come home ten pounds heavier with everyone saying, "Oh, it looks like you had a good time abroad!" So I did what felt good and safe:

I reverted back to some old tricks. Not all of them, but restriction became an ever-present thought once again.

I went to visit one of my best friends in France over spring break. Word travelled back home quickly. Caroline seems pretty thin. Are we sure she is okay? Do her parents know? I was about to have a conversation that brought all these questions into the light. Was I ready to truly face this lingering struggle? It didn't matter if I was ready; the time had come to face this demon once and for all.

THE PROS AND CONS LIST

This wasn't the conversation I was expecting.

Weekly I would call home on the pay phone outside my apartment to check in with my family. To fill them in on my European adventures. This time mom had some news for me.

My heart was beating fast as I hung up the pay phone on the busy streets of Madrid.

"You cannot go back to college if you are not doing well," Mom had said.

Her firm voice had just delivered a stinging ultimatum on the other end of the line. Word had gotten back to her that I was reverting back to some dangerous behaviors. Restricting food and losing more weight. Mom was not happy. My parents were done with this. There would be consequences if I continued, she said.

I knew all the right things to do. I had learned the tools to live free of anorexia, but I wasn't using them. I was terribly anxious and homesick. And I knew what I could do to manage those feelings. During these last few months in Spain, I hadn't gone completely back into the deep, dark world of an eating disorder, but I was flirting with it. Mostly apples for lunch, lots of Cafe Americanos to deal with the hunger pains. And I was now a vegetarian and eating the light vegetable soups Marite was making most nights for our evening meals. Even she found herself ten pounds thinner after adopting a vegetarian diet. I didn't expect to be found out. In fact, I was surprised the news that I was struggling again had travelled across the world.

That phone call with my mom brought me to the hard place of dealing with this once and for all. I had to. I knew too much at that point. I knew anorexia was a dead-end road, but why was I always so tempted by it? What was this really about? It was time to get real. I had to meet the monster head-on.

Right after that phone call with mom, I was scheduled to leave with a group of girls for the weekend. I didn't know them all that well, and I certainly wasn't going to talk about this new dilemma. A weekend of leisure and adventure, tapas and wine with almost strangers was absolutely not what I was in the mood to do. I was so preoccupied by the call that I could barely think about anything else.

We traveled by train to Torremolinos, a small coastal town not far from Madrid. This was the luxury of living abroad—we were encouraged to travel on the weekends and experience the unique and beautiful Spanish culture. "Seize the day!" they told us. I was living the life! Art museums, sidewalk cafes, leisurely walks on cobblestone streets in towns steeped in Spanish tradition, this was college living at its finest! But we all know outside appearances can be deceiving.

I felt alone. There was an odd number of us traveling, so I had a single room. "Oh great," I thought. "Even more alone time!" But this was a divine appointment with myself. I had some thinking to do. A decision to make. This was 1995, and I had no cell phone, so there was no texting friends or checking Instagram to see what your people were up to. That entire weekend I tried to contact some key people in my life via pay phone to get their thoughts on everything, to help me sort it out. I couldn't get in touch with anyone. It was like God was forcing me to be still with my thoughts. Imagine that! But I know He was there with me, orchestrating it all. He wanted me by myself. And He is good at getting what He wants.

The girls and I were staying at a simple hostel in Torremolinos. The first morning I went down to the quaint lobby to have coffee and to journal. A regular ritual of mine. But this morning of solitude was different. I held on to my Bible, my sacred journal, and my pen as I walked down the musky set of stairs to the small cafe. "Cafe Americano, por favor." Black coffee and blank pages. I had a serious date with my journal and Bible that morning. I needed to *see* what was going on inside my head. I needed to write down the battle that was raging in my heart. I knew it was time to decide which road I was going to pursue.

Of course, I knew the right things to do. I had learned them from the therapists, the nutritionists, the books, the programs. I knew that an eating disorder was wrong. But why did I continue to peer down this lonely road? What was it about being anorexic that continued to be appealing? I had to expose my true thoughts once and for all.

I opened God's Word and looked for answers. I was holding on for dear life. "He knows me, He loves me, He made me, He wants the best for me. And He keeps on pursuing me time and time again." I poured out these thoughts onto the journal pages. They were all things I knew to be true. But I also knew I couldn't have both God and my eating disorder. There just wasn't room for both. There was one throne in my heart, in all of our hearts, and only one master can live there. It was time for the final showdown: it was either God or my eating disorder. They could not coexist.

That's when it hit me. I needed to *see* what these two lives looked like. A life ruled by an eating disorder and a life free of its shackles.

There were two roads. One road that followed God and one road that followed the dark lure of anorexia. I had to see what these two roads looked like side by side. Expose them. So I did what many do when they want to simplify things when making a decision. I wrote a pros and cons list. The oldest trick in the book for making up your mind.

What were the pros of being anorexic? Well, there was only one.

PROS

- Forever thin. Super skinny.

That was it, the sole benefit. Everyone knows you don't eat the queso. You don't eat the cake. You are the disciplined one. The one who wears size zeros and never skips a day of exercise. The one that people admire for not indulging in pizza late night when you get home from a party. Not a life that screams fun or spontaneity. How do you have time for others if you are so worried about your own routines? How do you have time for really anything else?

So that was the first column I made. The next column was the cons to being anorexic.

CONS

- It will ultimately kill me.
- I can't have a meaningful relationship, let alone get married.

- It will be hard to have children when I can't even have a period.
- It's terrible for friendships.
- It is miserable to be that hungry.
- It's no fun to never let myself enjoy food or travel or spontaneity, etc.
- It makes God sad that I would be letting another god rule in my heart.

The list went on and on . . .

So I had two columns. A short one and a long one. And then I looked at the words on the page. Really looked at them. The right thing to do was obvious. There was no question that living without an eating disorder was the better path, the best path. It was the path to life. It was the path I knew I wanted to ultimately walk down. I wanted to be married, to have children, to be a good friend, and to love God with my whole heart. The path of anorexia was absurd. And I could see that now. I didn't decide right there and then, but I knew what my next step must be. I knew which road must be destroyed. Seeing the one pitiful benefit of being anorexic versus the costs was mind blowing. It was clear as day. Was I ready to do this? Was I ready to say goodbye to the darkness forever?

In Genesis 32, there is the famous story of Jacob wrestling with God all night. Until "daybreak," it says. This is what I felt like. I was wrestling. I knew it was time to lay down my eating disorder. I knew that holding on to any part of this addiction was unacceptable. I really did want to let it go, but I was scared. "Lord, can I really do this?" I prayed. "I want to, but I need you to help me!" God was right there with me. He led me to this place of solitude and sobriety. I began to see my pros and cons list as the key. Looking at it, memorizing it, and studying it allowed me to see the ignorance of doing anything else but throwing this eating disorder off a cliff to its certain death.

I sat with this new information. I didn't dare tell anyone yet. Was I ready to admit that I had seen the eating disorder for what it was? That it was a lie? That I was ready to let it go? Once I said it, I would be held accountable. Was I ready for that? I got out the pros and cons list again. I read it again. Oh, okay, that's right, I remember now, there is nothing good about it. I am ready. I want to go down the path of life, and good, and God. I know that is what I need to do, it's what I want to do, but I am so nervous. I trust you, help me trust you.

I was like the father from Mark 9:24, saying to Jesus, "I believe; help my unbelief!" My heart was exposed. I wanted God to *help me* want to be done with disordered eating. "I want to let go of this forever; help me want to let go of this forever," I prayed.

We have to get real with ourselves. We have to see that our efforts are meek and wishy washy and in need of His power. I was ready to give it up, but I needed Him to help me really give it up. That is where true recovery takes place: knowing your need and knowing that there is One who can help you in your most desperate hour.

That day I made the decision. I made the decision again about every five or ten minutes for a few weeks. Truly, I got that handwritten pros and cons list out of my back pocket fifty times a day for at least the first two weeks. There was a rewiring of my brain that needed to take place. I do believe that. I remember one day stopping at an intersection on a busy Madrid street, needing to read through the list. I kept forgetting why I wanted to get better. I had to remind myself right that second of what I was doing and why I was doing it.

Letting go is not easy. It is scary. It is new territory. You feel as if you are falling over a cliff, and you only hear the still, small voice from below saying that He will be there to catch you. And that voice is right. That voice is God. He was there to catch me. And day by day, brave step by brave step, I began to trust recovery, and I became healed.

THE SCALES FELL OFF

Paul's conversion in the book of Acts is a beautiful and dramatic story. He lost his sight for three days, but then the Lord sent a man to restore his ability to see, and Scripture says "something like scales fell from his eyes" (Acts 9:18). Paul could see. He was a new believer in Jesus and his sight was restored. He used to persecute Christians and then he became one. This story feels a lot like mine. All of a sudden, I could see. I decided to lay down my eating disorder. I wrestled with it for a while, like Jacob. And then I saw it clearly like Paul. It took a little while for me to really decide if I was going to do it. To let it die. That simple pros and cons list exposed the reality of what it was. It was the road to nowhere. The opposite of where I wanted to go.

After about a week of this new road, I did the next brave thing and let my parents know what had happened. I nervously called my mom and told her about my new clarity, the decision I had made. I knew once I told her, there was no going back. I would be held accountable for the new life I was going to live. My parents were of course thrilled, and probably skeptical. The day after I told them this news, they heard a sermon at church about Paul's scales falling from his eyes. It was another heavenly sign that God was in all the details. Mom felt like it was God telling her what had happened to me. She shed tears of joy and relief that day.

A few weeks after this milestone, I returned home to Austin from Spain. I was so ready to be with family and friends and normalcy. My parents insisted that I continue to work with a therapist that summer to make sure I was doing okay. "Let's double-check this isn't just a fleeting miracle," they thought. So I did. I saw a great therapist and joined a group of women who were working toward recovery. And you know what? I saw that I really was done with that old way of life. I heard their stories and remembered their struggles, but I was no longer there. I had escaped from the prison. I was outside the bars looking in and living in freedom. I wanted the same thing for those women. I continue to want freedom for everyone trapped in the prison—that's why I wrote this book!

I am not saying that recovery is simple. There are setbacks and temptations and slipups along the road. Plan on them. And know what you are going to do when you are tempted. That's a must. Know who you will call or what you will do when you feel the scary temptations of relapse. A couple years later, when I began to plan my dream wedding to marry my dream guy, I felt a temptation to revert to old ways. To look as perfect as possible, as thin as possible. It was my time to shine as the "perfect bride," right? Surely I could bring back just a few of my old tricks?

Planning a wedding is wonderful, but it can also produce anxiety. Old and familiar thoughts began to creep back into my mind, tempting me to starve myself for the big day. Just weeks before my wedding, I was in the shower and felt an overwhelming feeling of darkness hover

over me. I knew quite well who it was. I had listened to that cunning voice before, and I wasn't going to do it this time! I was a new person. I had my armor ready. A dear friend had taught me something that I had never tried before, but I knew it was my best weapon against this evil. I got down on my knees right there in the shower, and as the water ran over me, I said, "Satan be gone!" The darkness left. I told it to. The Holy Spirit fought for me, and we won. The dark voice of anorexia had no hold over me anymore. Another miracle. Another time that I refused to go down that dark path. I was not going to let those evil thoughts steal my joy! And guess what, they didn't.

I felt fabulous on my wedding day. And I ate the cake. Hallelujah!

I found a book around this same time entitled *Making Peace with Food* by Susan Kano. It had a goofy cover with an odd-looking lady shaking hands with a potato. Not the coolest looking book, but the premise was excellent. It really helped me hone in on some key concepts moving forward. No food was off-limits. That may sound like a no-brainer to some, but to me this was still a new concept. I took this book on my honeymoon, believe it or not. Sexy, right? It really helped to keep my mind filled with thoughts of freedom regarding food.

Here is a key to lasting recovery: keep learning. Keep reading about healthy mindsets. Keep your body healthy. Hang out with healthy people. And limit your time with unhealthy people. Make sure you learn what is a good environment for you. And be aware of what isn't a good environment. Know your triggers! If you are around people who complain about their body, maybe it's time to change the subject. Or change friends. Just be real with yourself. Feed your body and take care of your mind. Most importantly, know your limits. Recovery is a mindset and a journey. And the freedom is worth it!

IT'S A GIRL

My husband and I decided to start a family about five minutes after we got married. Not really, but I'm sure it seemed that way to those around us. We tied the knot in May, and in August we were both staring at a positive pregnancy test. We were ecstatic! I met with my OB soon after, and we discussed my history of anorexia and how that could impact my pregnancy. Gaining weight, craving all sorts of weird foods, was I ready for that? Turned out I *loved* being pregnant. It was humbling knowing my body was creating a miracle. It suddenly had such purpose! It was no longer about what I looked like—a child was being formed within me. Does it get any cooler than that?

Ten days after our first wedding anniversary, we welcomed our first child into this world. We didn't know the gender. The suspense was killing us, but we wanted to find out the old-fashioned way. Surely I would have a boy!

"It's a little girl!" My husband, West, choked out through precious tears.

I heard those stunning and surprising words while lying there on the operating table. I had just had my first C-section and was a little groggy when my world was forever changed with that incredible news. I was thrilled but also a tad concerned.

"God, are you sure I am ready for a girl? I really haven't been in recovery all that long."

These really were my first thoughts as I stared at my beautiful infant daughter. And yet, in that moment, it was like I heard God saying, "Yes, honey, I think you are ready. I know this seems like a lot for you, but I planned for this to be your little girl." It seemed like another step. A big step. He trusted me. And I knew I had a big responsibility.

I felt empowered. And a little nervous. Remember, it was just four years earlier that I was living in a world of darkness and dysfunction. But having a girl was like a vote of confidence, and it gave me a new sense of accountability. I desperately wanted this little girl to live in freedom. I didn't want her to experience what I had lived through. She was born with a clean slate, and I wanted to keep it that way!

Then two years later God did something really incredible and somewhat comical. He gave me another daughter. And then a few years after that, daughter number three.

When they were wheeling me back to my postpartum room after my third daughter was born, I passed my elated mom in the hallway of the hospital. She gasped when she saw me and said, "Oh, Caroline, you have won the lottery!" It was such a perfect comment. She grew up with four brothers and I grew up with two. Neither of us had had a sister. To think that I had three daughters was absolutely unimaginable to her. There are days when I do think I have won the lottery, and there are days when I am pretty sure ten boys would have been easier. But I still can't believe I get to raise three girls.

Four years after that, we added a fourth child to our family, and this time it was a son. All four of my children are so beautiful, so different, so unique. As a parent I have done some things well, and I could have done some things better. I can live with that. But I can say with assurance that I have raised them with great intentions regarding healthy eating and a healthy body image.

People have asked me when I decided to tell my kids about my eating disorder. Honestly, I don't remember a day they didn't know about it. It was just something I talked about honestly and openly. I can't put my finger on any one conversation, it was just a given that healthy attitudes about our bodies and our eating habits were what we aimed for. Dieting wasn't something we did. They knew my history and knew I would not tolerate a toxic atmosphere around food or our bodies. Here are some of the things I've done and continue to do to accomplish this.

I DON'T CRITICIZE MY BODY OUT LOUD

I can't swear that no critical words have ever escaped my lips, but overall I make great efforts to avoid talking about my body in a critical way. "Does this make me look fat?" is not a question my kids have ever heard me say. I may have wondered that in my head, but I didn't voice it to them. Body insecurity just wasn't something we talked about. Intentionally. There may have been times that I felt uncomfortable in my skin, but I really tried to not talk about that. I knew the world would make them question themselves enough. I wanted them to at least have a mom who was content with what she looked like.

I MAKE BEING HEALTHY A PRIORITY

I try to stay fit. I did and do exercise regularly. I think this is a good thing. Over the years I have become less enthusiastic about exercising, but I still try to do it. For me that looks like maybe a few times a week. Nothing crazy. Nothing extreme. Walking with friends, a yoga sculpt class, or running on the treadmill for thirty minutes with some weights after. Even if by some standards I could stand to exercise a little more, I would rather show them what it looks like to do *less*, not more. I wanted my daughters to see what a healthy lifestyle looked like in terms of exercise.

I DON'T BUY TRASHY MAGAZINES

Years ago when I was in the middle of raising three little girls, magazines were available on every grocery aisle, and they screamed to all women what we "should" look like. It was the equivalent to social media today, which of course is now accessible to everyone. Which makes raising girls even harder! But back then having those magazines around was something I *could* say no to. I remember many times telling the girls that I was not going to buy them even though it was tempting! Now, I am not going to say I never looked at them, but I didn't allow them in my house. I just felt like their message was detrimental to my girls. And honestly to mine as well. We need to know our boundaries. We need to protect our minds. This may look like limiting social media nowadays. You are the gatekeeper for their little eyes for a while. Protect them! Soon enough you will not be able to.

I DON'T USE A SCALE

At the height of my eating disorder, I sometimes weighed myself ten, twenty, even thirty times a day. Scales are a no for me. I don't weigh myself. It's just not necessary. My husband keeps one in his closet, so I don't think they are evil. But excessive weighing of yourself can send the wrong message, especially to your kids. If I have to get on the scale at the doctor, I turn around. Do I let those numbers bother me? Yes. They bother me. Seeing my weight is still a trigger for me. I don't need to know what I weigh. And I really didn't want my kids weighing themselves when they were young.

I TRY TO PRACTICE WHAT I PREACH

Moms, here is a question for you. What can you do to keep your children from obsessing about their bodies? There is only one thing you can truly do about that: don't obsess over yours. You don't want them to be controlled by what they eat? Then don't be controlled by what you eat.

We are their first up-close and personal example of how a woman accepts herself. How she lives in her skin, and how she takes care of her body. If you're thinking you have not done this well, there is grace for you. And it is never too late to start! Start today. Have lunch with your daughter like sweet Teenie did with me and say that you want to do things differently. Living in real freedom in this area of life is so awesome! I want you to experience this! Our bodies were made to move, to work, to love others, to serve others, to eat, to sleep, to be in relationship with other people. They are gifts! Let's treat them like that. I believe God gave us hunger and food to remind us how needy we are and how daily we come to the table to receive what we cannot live without.

It was kind of hilarious when I got married and realized that my husband's love language was dinner. Of course this recovering anorexic would marry someone who loved good dinners every night. Every *single* night. Again, I think it was God's plan of accountability. As a young bride I had to read the back of the pasta box to know how to boil noodles. Boy, have I improved. My entire family loves good food. Dinner is a big deal for the six of us. It has taken me a long time to get the cooking thing down, but now I am a great cook! Thanks to cutie pie Pioneer Woman Ree Drummond, I really have grown to love to cook for my family. Over the years I have poured over her colorful cookbooks, committing to memory her family's favorite recipes. She wasn't worried about fat grams or calories; her goal was to create meals that tasted great and truly nourished her farm-loving big family. That's the kind of cook I wanted to be. I still think her chicken enchiladas are the very best, and as a Texan I should know!

I like role models—real people who have lived life well. People we can point to and say that we hope to follow in their footsteps. Someone who has been this for me is the woman described in detail in Proverbs 31. Some people moan when they hear this reference, but I don't think they have looked hard enough at what she teaches us. This famous Bible passage begins with, "An excellent wife who can find?" We can immediately breathe a sigh of relief. We are automatically off the hook because this dream girl doesn't really exist! No one can really find her, she is just an example of who we are striving to be!

What I love most about this Proverbs 31 lady is how she can "laugh at the time to come." Think about that for a moment. What a picture of freedom. Someone who knows she is not in control, that she is comfortable enough in her maker that she can throw her head back and laugh about the future. What a picture of peace. Don't we all want that? I have moments when I feel that way, and it is joyful and exhilarating. She is a woman who knows who she is. She knows where she is going, what she is capable of here on this earth, and who is ultimately in control. That is someone living out the serenity prayer. She's a head back, laughing out loud, peace-filled, joy-filled woman. Sign me up for that life!

We are not in control, my friends. We never were and we never will be. And that is a good thing! Over and over again we are compared to sheep in God's Word. Sheep are lovely and darling and important, but they are not known for their intelligence. They need a shepherd, and God is a really good shepherd. He could have one hundred sheep in His flock but will go looking for just one if they are missing (Matthew 18:12). That is how important His sheep are to Him. God never stopped looking for me. Even when I chose darkness, even when I denied Him and dropped Him like a bad habit, He pursued me. He loved me enough to leave the ninety-nine and rescue me.

God loves you too. He wants you to lay down your burdens and rest. His yoke is easy and His burden is light. Doesn't that sound wonderful? Isn't that what we are looking for? Peace? Joy? Yes. He offers you just that. He has led me to both peace and joy once I laid down my old ways.

If you are living with an eating disorder, I challenge you to consider laying this burden down. Talk to someone. Talk to God. I know it is scary, but I promise you there is a better way. Make a pros and cons list. Look at the reality of the two paths. If you are honest with yourself, you will see that one way leads only to destruction. If you have a child with an eating disorder, keep praying, and talk with those who can encourage you and give you solid advice. There are so many people out there with wonderful wisdom who know how to help: counselors, therapists, nutritionists, professionals who are trained to help those caught in the snares of this addiction.

Thank you for hearing my story. You and I were made to be hungry. It's how we know we are alive. So let's walk down this path and live to the fullest! Let's dance and jump, love and serve, and eat some cake along the way! If God could lead me to recovery, He can lead anyone. I never thought this was possible. But with Him *all* things are possible! I can promise you that.

ENDNOTES

1 This quote has been attributed to various people over the decades. According to Quote Investigator, the most reasonable attribution is to Frank Outlaw, the late president of Bi-Lo stores: https://quoteinvestigator.com/2013/01/10/watch-your-thoughts/.

2 Solara Mental Health Writer. "Celebrities with OCD." *Solara Mental Health*, Staff Writer, 1 July 2022, https://solaramentalhealth.com/celebrities-with-ocd/.

3 "8 Odd Facts about Charles Dickens." Neatorama, December 9, 2010. https://www.neatorama.com/2008/05/26/8-odd-facts-about-charles-dickens/#:~:text=Dickens%20was%20preoccupied%20with%20looking,%2C%20he%20couldn't%20concentrate.

4 "10 Facts You Didn't Know about Michelangelo." DailyArt Magazine, February 24, 2022. https://www.dailyartmagazine.com/facts-didnt-know-michelangelo/.

5 "Our Work." National Eating Disorders Association, March 2, 2022. https://www.nationaleatingdisorders.org/about-us/our-work.

6 "Common Eating Disorders & Treatment Options: Eleanor Health." Eleanor Health - Recovery. For. Life., November 29, 2021. https://www.eleanorhealth.com/blog/eating-disorders#:~:text=10%2C200%20deaths%20each%20year%20are,disorders%2C%20behind%20opioid%20use%20disorder.

7 Noguchi, Yuki. "Eating Disorders Thrive in Anxious Times, and Pose a Lethal Threat." NPR. NPR, September 8, 2020. https://www.npr.org/sections/health-shots/2020/09/08/908994616/eating-disorders-thrive-in-anxious-times-and-pose-a-lethal-threat.

8 *Merriam-Webster*, s.v. "sophomore," accessed April 15, 2022, https://www.merriam-webster.com/dictionary/sophomore.

ACKNOWLEDGEMENTS

Wanting to write a book and actually writing one are two very different things. I think it is a lot like running a marathon. Lots of people talk about it, yet few people actually cross the finish line. Yes, you must have the desire to run, but next you need to devise a training plan, create a team of encouragers, and prepare for the actual race. It takes determination, discipline, and a clear plan of how to get your mind and body ready for utter exhaustion. Believe it or not this sounds a lot like writing a book. There is much more to it than just wanting to write. Over the past two years here are some of the people who helped make this book come alive.

To Noelle Warner - you have such a beautiful gift! You call yourself a "proper mirror" but you are so much more than that! The encouragement you gave me to write this book was paramount to beginning the process. And you were the one to tell me about Ally! So grateful for you!

To Ally Fallon and Annie Kyle and her team at Find Your Voice, I am forever grateful for you all! Your desire to help new authors like myself is such a gift - and I don't know if I could have ever gotten these words onto the page without your help! Keep doing what you are doing! Just imagine the books you are helping to create!

To Esther, Danielle, and the entire Fedd Agency! Thank you for coming in on a Saturday morning to talk to me and Mom about our many book projects! Your willingness to listen to our hearts and then take next steps were crucial for "Hungry" to enter the world! Thank you for taking a chance on me! And of course there is more to come!

To AJ Gregory - thank you for being willing to lend your talent during the all important editing process. Your comments were so encouraging and your edits pushed me to make the manuscript better and better. Let's do it again!

To my sweet mom. I know the scenes depicted in this book are not all great memories. As I wrote "Hungry" I realized how important your parenting was for me to reach true recovery. Your tough love was what it took for me to decide I wanted to get better once and for all. Thank you. I know Rob, Will and I would nominate you for the mom Hall of Fame if we could!

I am someone who loves a best friend. Someone you know is there for you no matter what. I had and still have that friend in Cynda. We met in first grade and have been thick as thieves ever since. You and your sisters have treated me like the fourth girl in your family, which has been such a blessing! And now I have sweet Kitsie. K - our daily early morning check ins are such a gift. You have walked and prayed alongside me during this entire project! I am forever grateful that the Lord has us doing life together! And Shelly you are like the little sister I never had. My girls think you are so cool they still cant believe you hang out with me. All of you have been such incredible cheerleaders during this process!

To my family, aka the Brookfield Ballers. It's hard to encourage a writer when you are not sure they are really a writer, but you all did. Girls - you told your friends about the book, and would call me sometimes just to tell me who "really needs to read it". Those words kept me going, knowing that it really did need to get out there in the world. Being the wife and mom of this wild beautiful bunch is my greatest claim to fame. I love you all more than you know!

And finally to Jesus. I still can't believe you really keep pursuing me time and time again. But that is who you are. Your word continues to teach me that you never stop loving, never stop forgiving, and never stop pouring out wisdom and mercy to your children. My ultimate hope is that readers will see more of who you are in these pages.

And to the reader, thank you for reading my story. Some of you may know what it is like to have an eating disorder, and some of you may have no clue what it is! But all of us know what it is like to feel uncertain about who we are as we face the great unknown. And really that is what this story is about. And the hero of the story is the very one who made you.

AUTHOR BIO

Caroline B Cook never meant to be a young mom, she thought she had way too much to do! But after falling in love with West at 22, she was married at 23 and excepting their first daughter at 24. Now they have been married for almost 25 years and have 3 almost grown daughters and one teenage son. Selling real estate, writing books, and teaching women about the goodness of God are a few of her favorite things. But she is happiest entertaining at home with plenty of friends and lots of Mexican food (and maybe some skinny margaritas).